PASS YOUR AMATEUR RADIO GENERAL CLASS TEST – THE EASY WAY

2023-2027 Edition

By: Craig E. "Buck," K4IA

ABOUT THE AUTHOR: "Buck," as known on the air, was first licensed in the mid-sixties as a young teenager. Today, he holds an Amateur Extra Class Radio License. Buck is an active instructor and a Volunteer Examiner. The Rappahannock Valley Amateur Radio Club has named him Elmer (Trainer) of the Year three times.

Email: K4ia@EasyWayHamBooks.com

Published by EasyWayHamBooks.com
130 Caroline St. Fredericksburg, Virginia 22401

Easy Way Books by Craig Buck are available from Amazon, Barnes & Noble, Ham Radio Outlet and Gigaparts:
"Pass Your Amateur Radio Technician Class Test"
"Pass Your Amateur Radio Extra Class Test"
"How to Chase, Work & Confirm DX"
"How to Get on HF"
"Prepper Communications"
"Pass Your GROL General Radiotelephone Operator License Test"

Library of Congress Control Number: 20239026961

ISBN: 979-8-9856739-2-0

PASS YOUR AMATEUR RADIO GENERAL CLASS TEST – THE EASY WAY

TABLE OF CONTENTS

TABLE OF CONTENTS

INTRODUCTION

There are many books and methods to study for amateur radio exams. Most take you through the 430[1] questions and all possible answers on the multiple-choice test. The problem with that approach is that you must read three wrong answers for every one right answer. That's 1,720 answers, of which 1,290 are wrong and only 430 correct. No wonder people get overwhelmed.

This book is unique. There are no confusing wrong answers to bog you down. I'll explain every question on the General Class exam to help you understand and recognize the correct answers.

There are three paths. First, an explanation of concepts with the test questions and answers in **bold print**. Hints to remember the answers are in *italic print*.

Second, each chapter ends with a condensed one-line summary for every question and answer.

Third, the last part of this book is a Review with only the question and correct answer.

You will pass your General Class exam, but the test does not tell you how to operate, choose equipment, and put up antennas. Be sure to check out my other books: "***How to Get on HF – The Easy Way***" for detailed instructions to get on the air and "***How to Chase, Work and Confirm DX – The Easy Way***" to enter the exciting world of DX. Go to EasyWayHamBooks.com or scan this code.

---

[1] Originally 432, but two were deleted.

HOW YOU SHOULD STUDY

To ace a multiple-choice exam, learn to recognize, not memorize, the correct answer. Plus, don't study the wrong answers!

EasyWayHamBooks are All Ham and No Spam®[2]. There are no confusing, wrong answers. The correct answer should pop out when you see it on the test because you have never seen the wrong answer. You do not need to memorize the whole question and answer—just enough to recognize the right answer.

<u>Do not take practice exams until after you have mastered the material.</u> Seeing wrong answers is not the way to learn. I know curiosity will get the best of you, but please do not take practice exams until the week before the test, and <u>after</u> you feel you know this material. Recognize the correct answers first. Take the practice exams if you must, only as a confidence builder, not to study.

Your amateur radio license is called a "ticket." A ticket begins a journey. You can't start a journey without one. Likewise, you need a ticket to start your amateur radio journey. Get your ticket, and the rest of the details will come later. There is plenty to learn, and you have the rest of your life to do it.

If you are stuck on a question or concept, visit my Facebook group "Ham Radio Exams." You will find plenty of folks happy to assist and encourage.

---

[2] "All Ham and No Spam" is a registered to EasyWayHamBooks with the US Patent and Trademark Office.

THE TEST

The test is 35 questions from a pool of 432. Every four years, the National Conference of Volunteer Examiners publishes a new pool of questions and answers. This book is for tests from July 1, 2023 to June 30, 2027. Check the NCVEC.org website for any corrections since this book's printing.

We know the exact wording of the questions and answers in advance. The test jumbles the answer's order. Answer "A" might not be "A" on your exam, but the wording will be the same.

There are 35 test-subject groups, and the test has one question from each group. While the pool is large, only about one in a dozen questions will show be on the test. There will not be 35 questions on one topic.

Learn it all, but there is only one question from each group. If there is a question or concept, you cannot get or memorize, don't worry. Chances are, it will not be on the test. 92% of the questions in the pool will <u>not</u> be on your test. You can miss 9 of the 35 questions and still pass. You only need to know 6% (26 out of 432) of the answers in the pool. Name another test where a score of 6% is a passing grade. Miss every math question and still pass. Do your best, but don't sweat it.

What do they call the medical student who graduates last in the class? "Doctor," the same as the person who graduates first in the class. Pass and you'll be a General. No one will ever know your score.

So, how hard is the General test? It is more challenging than the Technician with a bit more memorizing, but you can do it. I have taken students who knew nothing about electronics, radio, or math through this material, and they passed.

THE TEST

Most important: when the day comes, take the test even if you don't feel ready. You are better prepared than you think and will probably pass.

There is no Morse code (CW) required for any class of amateur license. Morse code is still very much alive and well on the amateur bands, and there are many reasons to learn it in the future. Just don't worry about it for now. A chapter on learning CW is at the end of this book.

The questions are multiple choice, so you do not have to know every word of the answer, <u>only enough to recognize it</u>. That is a tremendous advantage for the test-taker. However, studying the multiple-choice format can get one bogged down and confused by seeing three wrong answers for every correct one. Studying wrong answers makes it harder to recognize the right answer.

The best way to study for a multiple-choice exam is to concentrate on the correct responses. Find a recognizable word or phrase. When you take the test, the correct answer should jump out. The wrong ones will seem strange and unfamiliar. Don't overthink. Trust your instinct.

If you do not recognize the answer, eliminate the obviously wrong ones, and then guess. There is no penalty for guessing wrong. The answer is often common sense and logic, not engineering. Learn to recognize or figure out the answer.

Long ago, when my friend Billy and I sat for our General test, we took a bus to the FCC Building in Washington, DC. There, we met the sternest proctor I have ever suffered. Picture the short-sleeve white shirt, hairy arms, skinny black tie, pocket protector, slide-rule-on-the-belt, thick eyeglasses, scowl, dangling cigarette, and a full ashtray. I was sure the

FBI told him I had listened to Radio Moscow. If I did not pass the test, I was going straight to jail.

Today, Volunteer Examiners (VEs) administer the testing. **Volunteer Examiners are accredited by a Volunteer Examiner Coordinator**[3] organized under the authority of the FCC. VEs are hams who devote their time to help you get your license. The ARRL website at arrl.org (click on the Licensing tab) lists local test sessions. W5YI.org also lists exam locations. There are others. Some groups test online.

A modest fee of about $15 reimburses the VE's costs — no one profits except you. The Laurel VE group tests for free.

You might not need to take the General Class test. An applicant can reinstate an expired license **by showing proof they once held a license grant and passing the current element 2 Exam.** That would be the Technician Class test.

On test day, bring a picture ID, the Federal Registration Number assigned when you registered for the Technician exam[4], a pen and pencil, and the exam fee. Check ahead to get the exact amount and ask if the VE Team prefers cash or check. You will need an email address for the application.

If you bring a calculator, you must show the VEs you have cleared the memories. Turn off your cell phone, put it in your pocket, and don't look at it during the exam.

---

[3] Bold print is a question and answer from the exam.

[4] Search "FCC ULS" to find the link to the FCC database or use the QR code above. Then search by "LastName, FirstName" to find your FRN.

THE TEST

An application (FCC Form 605) is available on the FCC website. Complete it beforehand to save time on test day.

The Volunteer Examiner team will select a test booklet. They do not know which questions are in which booklet. There is a multiple-choice, fill-in-the-circle answer sheet with room for 50 questions, but you stop at 35. Take notes and calculate on the back of the answer sheet, not in the booklet. The VEs re-use the booklets. Write memorized formulas on the back of the answer sheet immediately, before you forget or get confused.

The VE team grades the exam while you wait and gives a pass/fail result. Please, don't ask them to go over the questions or tell what you missed. They don't know and don't have time to look. After passing, you receive a CSCE – a Certificate of Successful Completion of Examination.

Your CSCE is valid for exam credit for 365 days. The team sends Form 605 and the CSCE to the FCC, and your new license class appears in the online database in a few days. Congratulations.

Once you pass your test and have your CSCE for General Class privileges, you can operate on any Technician or General Class band segment even before appearing as a General in the FCC database. Until you appear, **use the special identifier "AG" after your call sign when you operate using General Class privileges.** That would be W3ABC/AG. W3ABC stroke/slash/slant AG. After you show up in the FCC database, drop the AG.
Hint: Awaiting General.

Enough about the test. On to the test material...

G1 – COMMISSION'S RULES

Subelement G1 covers FCC rules. It has 5 groups. The test will have one question from each group. This pattern repeats with subsequent subelements and groups.

G1A – Frequency privileges; primary and secondary allocations

Begin at the beginning and review some basic theory. Radio waves act like an alternating current. The direction of flow reverses in cycles, unlike direct current from a battery, which flows in one direction only.

Frequency is the term describing the number of times per second that an alternating current completes a cycle. We measure frequency in cycles per second. The term Hertz is a shortcut for "cycles per second." The unit of frequency is Hertz.

Radio waves travel at the speed of light, 300 million meters per second. If we know the frequency is 150 Megahertz (150 million cycles per second), we can calculate how far the wave will travel in one cycle. 300/150 = 2 meters per cycle. Wavelength is the distance a radio wave travels during one complete cycle.

The higher the frequency, the more often the wave reverses direction, and the less distance it can travel in a cycle. Therefore, the wavelength gets shorter as the frequency increases.

The easy formula to convert the frequency to wavelength is "wavelength in meters = 300 divided by frequency in Megahertz." For example, if the frequency is 5 MHz, the wavelength is 300, divided by

5 or 60 meters. The same formula works in reverse: "Divide 300 by the wavelength in meters" to determine frequency. 300/60 meters = 5 MHz

A "band" is a group of frequencies. The approximate wavelength is often used to identify the different frequency bands. For example, "40 meters" for the 7–7.3 MHz band (300/7.3 = about 41). The math doesn't work out exactly. Round it off to 40 meters. The point here is to get close. If the question asks for the 40-meter band, you should know that 40 MHz is not a potential answer. After a while, you will recognize the various bands and the associated frequencies. There are not that many.

A General Class amateur radio license allows you to transmit on all bands. However, not all frequencies within the bands are available to General Class operators. Most bands reserve a part for Amateur Extra license holders.

Smart hams keep a chart handy because it is easier than memorizing the restrictions. However, several possible test questions ask you to recall band privileges.

A General Class license holder cannot transmit on portions of 80 meters, 40 meters, 20 meters, and 15 meters.
Hint: You do not need to memorize all this. Look for the only answer with 80 and 40 meters.

The bands with segments allocated to Amateur Extras are 80, 40, 20 and 15. Same answer.

Phone operation is prohibited on 30 meters.
Image transmission is prohibited on 30 meters.
30 meters (10.1 MHz) is for Morse code and digital modes only.

Hint: If something is "prohibited," the test answer is "30 meters."

A channel is a specific frequency. Most ham bands allow tuning to any frequency rather than a channel. **Communication is restricted to specific channels, rather than a frequency range on 60 meters.** (300/60 = 5 MHz).
Hint: Remember, 60 meters has specific channels.

A General Class license may not be a control operator between 7.125 and 7.175 MHz.
Those frequencies are reserved for Extra Class ops.
Cheat: Recognize the answer with 7 MHz.

Amateurs share some frequencies with other services. **When Amateur Service is designated as a secondary user, Amateur stations can use the band if they do not cause harmful interference to the primary users and must accept interference from primary users.**
Hint: Don't memorize all this. Recognize that, as secondary users, we must give way to primary users.

A General Class operator may transmit in the entire 10-meter band.

A General Class frequency within the 15-meter band is 21300 kHz.
Hint: The only test answer in the 15-meter band.

The portion of the 10-meter band available for repeaters is above 29.5 MHz. 10-meter Repeaters are at the top end of the band.

When Generals cannot use the whole band, the portion available is the upper-frequency end. Generals stay in the upper end of both the CW and voice segments.

G1B – Antenna structure limitations; good engineering practices, beacons, prohibited transmissions and retransmitting

Towers over 200 feet or near airports have limitations. **The maximum height above ground for an antenna structure without requiring notification to the FAA, provided you are not near a public-use airport, is 200 feet.** *Hint: Just look for 200 feet in an answer.*

"Broadcasting" refers to one-way transmitting to listeners. Hams can't broadcast, they two-way communicate. There are three exceptions to the rule against broadcasting.
One-way transmissions are permitted to assist in learning International Morse code. The rules allow code-practice sessions.

Another exception is for beacons. Two volunteer organizations operate a beacon network that broadcasts from different parts of the world on a ten-second rotating schedule. Each station identifies in Morse code at 100 watts and then sends dashes at 10 watts, 1 watt, and 100 milliwatts (1/10 watt). If you can hear the beacon, you know the band is open to that part of the world. There are other beacon stations, as well.
The purpose of a beacon station is observation of propagation and reception.

There must be no more than one beacon signal transmitting in the same band from the same location. *Hint: Doesn't that make sense?*

The third exception to the rule against broadcasting is **occasional retransmission of weather and propagation forecast information from US Government stations.**

Local governments may permit and regulate amateur radio antenna structures but must reasonably accommodate, and regulations must constitute the minimum practical to accommodate a legitimate purpose of the state or local entity.
Hint: Look for "reasonably accommodate" as the answer. Homeowner associations do not have to be reasonable or accommodate.

Rules do not allow ciphers and secret codes. Some abbreviations and procedural signals are in common use and don't obscure the meaning, so they are allowed.
Abbreviations and procedural signals may be used if they do not obscure the meaning of a message.
Hint: Do not obscure the meaning.

It is permissible to communicate with amateur stations in other countries except those who have notified the ITU they object to such communications.
You can talk to anyone unless that country objects. North Korea prohibits amateur radio, and you cannot communicate with someone there if you heard them (which you won't).

Automatically controlled beacons are permitted from 28.20 MHz to 28.30 MHz. They are also permitted on other bands, typically in the middle of the band.

The power limit for beacon stations is 100 watts.

We are required to follow good engineering and good amateur practice. **The FCC determines good engineering and good amateur practice.**
Hint: The FCC regulates the amateur service.

G1C – Transmitter power regulations; data emission standards; 60-meter operation

PEP is a measure of Peak Envelope Power.

The FCC rules regulating maximum power refer to PEP output from the transmitter.
Hint: Maximum power measured by "peak output."

The maximum power on 10.140 MHz is 200 watts. The 30-meter band is shared, limited to CW and data, and a maximum power of 200 watts.

"Bandwidth" describes how much room a signal takes, how wide it is.
The maximum bandwidth permitted on USB on 60 meters is 2.8 kHz.
Hint: The question gives the answer. USB is upper sideband, and a single sideband signal is 2.8 kHz wide.

The maximum power on the 60-meter band is an ERP of 100 watts with respect to a dipole.
The 30 and 60-meter bands are shared and limited. ERP is "effective radiated power," the total of the amplifier output and antenna gain. On 60 meters, you can run 100 watts to a dipole. You cannot run 100 watts to an antenna with more concentrated power (gain) than a dipole.

When operating in the 60-meter band, the FCC rules require you to keep a record of the gain of your antenna.
This is because of the effective-radiated-power restriction on 60 meters.

On the 12-meter band, the power limit is 1,500 watts.
On the 28 MHz band, the power limit is 1,500 watts.
On the 1.8 MHz band, the power limit is 1,500 watts.

Hint: The power limit is 1,500 watts except on 10.140 MHz (200 watts) and 60 meters (100 watts).

You cannot obscure the meaning of a message, and digital modes are not decipherable without the key. **Before using a new digital protocol on the air, the technical characteristics of the protocol must be publicly documented.** That is a job for the developers of the protocol.
Hint: Look for "publicly documented."

Data and RTTY (Teletype) signals get wider with faster symbol transmission rates. The allowable symbol rate is low on narrow HF bands to keep the signal from taking too much space. "Baud," bits per second, is the measure of the symbol rate.

The maximum symbol rate permitted for RTTY or data emission below 28 MHz is 300 baud.

The maximum symbol rate on the 10-meter band is 1200 baud."
Hint: Faster because the 10-meter band is wider.

G1D – Volunteer Examiners; VE coordinators; temporary identification; element credit.

Count yourself fortunate that you do not have to travel to an FCC Field Office for your test. The FCC turned testing responsibilities over to Volunteer Examiner Coordinators in 1984. There are about 14 Volunteer Examiner Coordinator organizations, and they jointly write the question pools and administer the system. The folks you see on test day are Volunteer Examiners.

If you had a license before as a General or above, you can regain your previous license class. Contact your local VE team for details.

COMMISSION'S RULES

Any person may receive partial credit for elements represented by an expired license, after the two -year grace period has expired, if they can demonstrate they once held a General, Advanced or Amateur Extra license that was not revoked by the FCC.
Hint: "not revoked."

Specifically, **you must show proof of the appropriate expired license grant and pass the Element 2 (Technician class) exam.**

VEs, Volunteer Examiners, are accredited by a Volunteer Examiner Coordinator. The FCC authorizes Volunteer Examiner Coordinators to coordinate and accredit individual examiners.

There must be at least three VEs present to administer a test. Multiple examiners assure the integrity of the system.
To administer a Technician class license examination, at least three General class or higher VEs must observe the examination.

The minimum age for a VE is 18 years.

A non-US citizen may be a VE if they hold an FCC granted license of General class or above.

VEs may only conduct tests for license classes below their own (except Extras because there is no higher license).
If you are a VE holding a General class license, you can administer a test to Technicians only.

A person must have a General class or higher license and VEC accreditation to administer a Technician class exam.
Hint: Same question.

Upon passing, the successful candidate receives a CSCE, Certificate of Successful Completion.
The CSCE is good for 365 days.

The VE team will submit the CSCE to the FCC and you can operate as a General immediately.
If you are a Technician class operator with a CSCE for the General class, you can operate on any General or Technician class band segment.

You identify by adding "AG" after your call sign while waiting for the FCC to post your upgrade on its website.
Hint: Awaiting General.

Remote control is twiddling the knobs from afar. The location of the transmitter determines licensing requirements.
When operating a US station by remote control from outside the country, the control operator must have a US operator/ primary station license.

When operating a station in South America by remote control over the Internet from the US, the applicable regulations are only those of the remote station's country.

G1E – Control categories; repeater regulations, third party rules; ITU regions, automatically controlled digital station

Third-party traffic is a non-ham speaking through your station. For example, you might have an unlicensed friend in your shack[5] and allow him to say hello to

[5] The radio shack on a ship is the room where the radios are located. "Shack" is the term used for the place from which you operate your radio.

another station. The United States allows third-party traffic, but some foreign countries prohibit it. **When third-party is allowed, messages must relate to amateur radio or remarks of a personal character, or emergencies or disaster relief.**

A third party would be disqualified from participating in stating a message over an amateur station if their amateur license has been revoked and not reinstated.
A revoked license bans you, even as a third party.

You learned the concept of a control operator on the Technician test. There are only two control operator questions on the General.

Technicians have limited privileges on 10 meters, but no privileges in the repeater portion of the 10-meter band.
A 10-meter repeater may retransmit the 2-meter signal from a station that has a Technician class control operator only if the 10-meter repeater control operator holds at least a General class license.

If there is a 10-meter repeater in the question, you know **the control operator for the 10-meter repeater must have at least a General Class license**.
This tricky question has been on the test for years.
Hint: Tie 10-meter repeater and General Class license together. Don't get distracted by the rest of the question.

There is another confusing control question that asks about a **digital station operating under automatic control outside the automatic control band segments**. **The station initiating the contact must be under local or remote control.**

Hint: It is outside the automatic control segments, so it must be under one of the other forms of control: local or remote.

Conditions that require you to take specific steps to avoid harmful interference to other users or facilities include:
When operating within one mile of an FCC Monitoring Station
When using a band where the Amateur Service is secondary
When transmitting spread spectrum emissions[6]
All these choices are correct
Hint: Do not memorize all these. Just recognize that any could cause interference, and you must take specific steps to avoid that.

The maximum PEP output allowed for spread spectrum transmissions is 10 watts.

The frequency allocations for ITU Region 2 apply to radio amateurs in North and South America.
Hint: ITU (International Telecommunication Union) Region 2.

Amateurs share part of the 2.4 GHz band with Wi-Fi routers.
An amateur station may not communicate with non-licensed Wi-Fi stations on any part of the band.
When operating as a ham, you cannot communicate with non-licensed services.

---

[6] Actress Hedy Lamarr is credited with developing spread-spectrum frequency hopping during WWII as a jam-proof way to steer torpedoes.

COMMISSION'S RULES

Part 97 of the Code of Federal Regulations governs amateur radio.
There are no circumstances when messages sent via digital modes are exempt from Part 97 regulations.
Hint: Part 97 always applies.

Beacons operate to test propagation. If you hear the beacon, you know propagation is open to that part of the world.
An amateur should avoid transmitting on 14.100, 18.110, 21.250, 24.930, and 28.200 MHz because a system of propagation beacons operates on those frequencies.
Hint: You do not need to memorize the frequencies. Avoid specific frequencies because of beacons.

Automatically controlled stations don't listen to see if a frequency is in use before transmitting, so rules limit their operation.
Automatically controlled stations may communicate with other automatically controlled stations in the 6-meter or shorter wavelength bands and in limited segments of some HF bands.
Hint: "Limited to limited segments."

An operator controlling the transmitter from a remote location, is "remote control."
Third-party messages may be transmitted via remote control under any circumstances in which third-party messages are permitted by the FCC rules. In other words, third-party messages sent by a remote control station follow the same rules as local control.

SUMMARY: COMMISSION'S RULES

GROUP A – FREQUENCY PRIVELEGES.

Generals cannot transmit on portions of 80,40,20 and 15 meters. Allocated to Amateur Extras.

General cannot be a control operator between 7.125 and 7.175 MHz

Phone and image prohibited on 30 meters.

Channels on 60 meters.

Secondary use may not interfere.

General may transmit on the entire 10-meter band.

Allowable General frequency is 21300 kHz.

Portion of 10 meters for repeaters is above 29.5 MHz.

Generals operate in the upper frequency end of a band.

GROUP B – ANTENNAS, BEACONS, BROADCASTING

Max antenna height 200 feet.

Local governments must reasonably accommodate.

No broadcasting except beacons, Morse code training, and rebroadcast of weather and forecasts from government stations.

One beacon at a time.

Beacons between 28.20 and 28.30 MHz.

Maximum beacon power 100 watts.

Abbreviations and procedural signals may not obscure the meaning.

Communicate with all countries except those who object.

FCC determines good practices.

GROUP C – POWER, DATA, 60 METERS

Maximum power measured in PEP.

Maximum power on 10.140 MHz is 200 watts.

COMMISSION'S RULES

On 60 meters, maximum power is 100 watts with respect to a dipole. Keep a record of the gain of your antenna.

On 12 meters, maximum power is 1500 watts.

On 28 MHz band maximum power is 1500 watts.

On 1.8 MHz band maximum power is 1500 watts.

Data modes must be publicly documented.

Maximum symbol rate below 28 MHz is 300 baud.

Maximum symbol rate in the 10-meter band is 1200 baud.

GROUP D – VOLUNTEER EXAMINERS

May receive credit on proof un-revoked prior license and pass Element 2.

Volunteer Examiners accredited by the Volunteer Examiner Coordinator.

Three VEs to administer a test.

Minimum VE age is 18.

VE may be in non-US citizen with a General class license or above.

Must have a General Class or above license to administer a Technician exam

CSCE is good for 365 days.

Can operate in the General portions with a CSCE. Identify by adding AG after your call.

Remote control rules follow where the transmitter is located.

Operating a US station by remote control requires a US license.

GROUP E – CONTROL, THIRD-PARTY, ITU REGIONS, AUTOMATIC CONTROL

Third-party traffic must relate to amateur radio, personal remarks or disaster relief.

Third party disqualified if their license has been revoked and not reinstated.

10-meter repeater requires a General Class license. Digital station outside the automatic control segments must be on local or remote control.

Avoid harmful interference when operating within one mile of FCC, when using a secondary band, or when using spread spectrum.

Maximum PEP for spread spectrum is 10 watts.

North and South America are ITU Region 2.

An amateur station may not communicate with a non-licensed station.

Avoid transmitting on beacon frequencies.

Automatically-controlled stations may communicate with each other on 6 meters and above and in limited segments of some HF bands.

Third-party messages may transmit by remote control where third party messages are allowed by FCC rules.

G2 - OPERATING PROCEDURES

G2A – Phone operating; USB/LSB conventions; breaking into a contact; transmitter setup for voice operation; answering DX stations

This figure of an Amplitude Modulated Signal shows two identical envelopes, one on each side of the center line. They are "sidebands." They contain the same information, so you can eliminate one sideband and the carrier without losing the message.

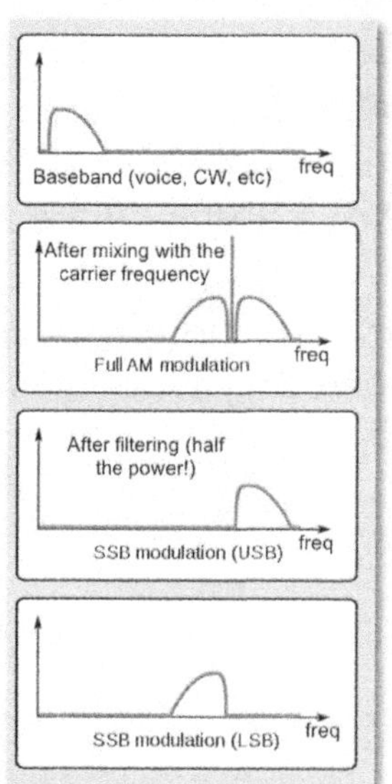

With single sideband (SSB), only one sideband is transmitted; the other sideband and carrier are suppressed.
Hint: It is single.

The voice mode most commonly used today is single sideband.

An advantage of single sideband is less bandwidth and greater power efficiency.
Hint: Less bandwidth and greater efficiency is an advantage.

The transmitted sideband could be on the upper or lower side of the carrier. You will hear this referred to as upper sideband or lower sideband.

By convention, the lower frequencies use lower sideband.
Voice communications on the 160-meter, 75-meter and 40-meter bands use lower sideband.

75 meters refers to the phone section of the 80-meter band.

Why? It is commonly accepted amateur practice. (Everyone does it).

Higher frequencies use upper sideband.
Upper sideband (USB) is normally used for 14 MHz and higher.
Upper sideband on 17-meter and 12-meter bands.
Upper sideband on VHF and UHF.
Hint: Lower sideband on 160, 75, and 40. Everything else is upper sideband.

To break into a phone contact, say your call sign once.
(Just like on the repeater). No "Breaker Breaker."

VOX uses your voice to activate the transmitter, versus PTT, which is Push to Talk.
VOX (Voice Operated Relay) allows hands-free operation.

If a station in the US calls "CQ DX," only stations outside the lower 48 states should respond.
He is asking for other countries.

The ALC (Automatic Level Control) circuit throttles back the drive to prevent distortion on the transmitted signal.
For the proper ALC setting, adjust the transmit audio or microphone gain.

G2B – Operating effectively; band plans; drills and emergencies; RACES operation

We all share the ham bands. If asked to move to accommodate a net or another conversation, courtesy dictates you should, but no one owns a frequency.

OPERATING PROCEDURES

Except during emergencies, no amateur station has priority access to any frequency.

If you are in a conversation and hear a station in distress break in, the first thing you should do is acknowledge the station in distress and determine what assistance may be needed.
Hint: Acknowledge and help.

If propagation changes and you notice interference from other stations, attempt to resolve the problem in a mutually acceptable manner.
When propagation changes, your "clear" frequency may get crowded. Be polite. Work it out. Outsmarting changing conditions is part of the fun.

A practical way to avoid interference before calling CQ is to send "QRL?" on CW, followed by your call sign; or, if using phone, ask if the frequency is in use, followed by your call sign.
Hint: Ask first or get yelled at later. "QRL?" means, "Is the frequency in use?

Don't get too close to an existing conversation, or you will interfere.
The minimum separation on CW is 150–500 Hz.
The minimum separation on SSB is approximately 3 kHz.
Hint: In each case, the answer closest to the actual bandwidth for the mode.

Commonly accepted amateur practice when choosing a frequency on which to call, is to follow the voluntary band plan for the operating mode you intend to use.
Hint: It makes sense to go where everyone is expecting you.

The voluntary band plan for the 48 states reserves 50.1 to 50.125 MHz only for contacts not within the 48 states.
That is the DX window for 6 meters, and it is the only band plan you need to know for the test. *Hint: Don't memorize the frequencies; recognize the question, and the answer is "not within the 48 states."*

RACES[7] is a volunteer organization that may provide amateur radio communications during emergencies. **The control operator of an amateur station transmitting in RACES to assist relief operations must hold an FCC amateur operator license.**
Hint: It is an amateur station, so the operator must hold an FCC amateur license. Being a government official is not enough.

RACES may conduct training drills without special authorization no more than one hour per week.

Good amateur practice for net management is having a backup frequency in case of interference or poor conditions.
Hint: The net must go on and needs a backup plan.

G2C – CW operating procedures and procedural signals; Q signals; full break-in

QSK describes switching from transmit to receive quickly, so you can hear between the dits and dahs as they are sent.
With full break-in CW operation (QSK), transmitting stations can receive between code characters and elements.
Hint: The received signal breaks in.

---

[7] Radio Amateur Civilian Emergency Service created by FEMA, the Federal Emergency Management Agency

OPERATING PROCEDURES

If a CW station sends "QRS," send slower.
Hint: QRSlower.

"QRL" means "Are you busy?" or "Is the frequency in use?"
If you send QRL? on CW and hear a response of "R" (Roger) or "C" (Confirm), the frequency is in use.

The best speed to answer a CQ in Morse code is the fastest you can do, but no faster than the CQ.
The caller sent at his comfort level. Don't exceed it.

"Zero beat" means matching the transmit frequency to the frequency of the received signal.
On CW, the receive and transmit tones match when you are on the same frequency.

A CW signal report consists of three numbers. The first digit is "readability" on a scale of 1-5. The second digit is "strength" on a scale of 1-9. The third digit is "tone" on a scale of 1-9. So, 599 is an excellent signal report - 100% readable, very strong, and a pure tone. **If you add a "C" at the end of the RST report, it means the other station has a chirpy or unstable signal.**
Hint: C as in chirp.

A prosign is a combination of letters sent as one (no spacing). Prosigns and Q signals are a universal language and abbreviation used mainly on CW but often heard on voice modes.

The prosign ending a formal CW message is AR.
Hint: All Remitted.

KN at the end of a transmission means listening for a specific station.
Hint: N = No one else.

The Q signal "QSL" means I have received and understood. It is the CW equivalent of 10-4 or Roger.

"QRN" means I am troubled by static.
Hint: QRNoise

"QRV" means I am ready to receive messages.
Hint: ReceiVe.

G2D – Volunteer Monitoring Program; HF Operations

Amateur radio is mostly self-regulating. Volunteer Monitors send out postcards to offenders, reminding them of the rules. They also congratulate good operators.
The Volunteer Monitoring Program is volunteers who are formally enlisted to monitor for rules violations.

The objectives of the Volunteer Monitoring Program are to encourage amateur radio operators to self-regulate and comply with the rules.
Hint: Look for "self-regulate."

If a continuous carrier is holding a repeater open, Volunteer Monitors might compare beam headings with other Volunteer Monitors to locate a station.
Directional antennas provide a beam heading and the offender is where the headings converge (triangulation).

An azimuthal projection map shows true bearings and distances from a particular location.
Azimuth is direction. You are in the center, and the map shows which way to point.

OPERATING PROCEDURES

If you are looking for a contact with any station on the HF phone bands, repeat "CQ" a few times, followed by "this is" then your call sign a few times, then pause and listen, repeat as necessary.
Hint: Look for the answer with "CQ" in it. If you are looking for contact with any station, call CQ. For example, "CQ CQ CQ. This is Kilo Four India Alpha, Kilo Four India Alpha, standing by for a call."

To make a long-path contact with another station, point your antenna 180 degrees from the short-path heading.
Hint: You are looking in the opposite direction, the long path around Earth.

A standard phonetic alphabet makes it easier to communicate. There are several, and the NATO version is favored.
Examples of the NATO alphabet are Alpha, Bravo, Charlie, Delta.
Hint: NATO is international, Alpha and Delta are Greek. Look for Alpha in the answer.

The reason many amateurs keep a log is to help with a reply if the FCC requests information.
That is the test answer. The FCC does not require you to keep a station log. I keep one to track award progress and remember contacts. I also add newsworthy items, such as when I get new equipment or change something at the station.

Radiosport is very popular, and there are several contests every weekend.
When you participate in a contest, you must identify your station per normal FCC regulations.
Hint: FCC regulations always apply.

QRP operation is low-power transmit operation.
Hint: QRPower.

Signal reports are typically exchanged at the beginning of an HF contact to allow each station to operate according to conditions.
A low signal report would tell you to increase power or turn a rotatable antenna.

G2E – Digital mode operating procedures

RTTY is Teletype, two modulating tones decoded as letters at the receiving end. AFSK uses audio frequency-shift keying, to generate those tones.
The most common frequency shift for amateur RTTY is 170 Hz.

When sending RTTY via AFSK use LSB (lower sideband).
Unlike voice, RTTY AFSK is always LSB. All other digital modes are USB.

If you can't decode an RTTY or other FSK (Frequency Shift Keying) signal even though it is apparently tuned in properly:
The mark and space frequencies may be reversed[8]
You may have selected the wrong baud rate
You may be listening on the wrong sideband.
All these choices are correct
Hint: Operator error is the leading cause of all errors.

Winlink is:
An amateur network to send and receive email on the Internet.
A form of Packet Radio (Packet is digital data sent in bursts or packets)
A wireless network capable of both VHF and HF band operation
All of the above

---

[8] Mark and space are names for the two tones.

OPERATING PROCEDURES

Another name for a Winlink Remote Message Server is a Gateway.
The remote message server acts as a gateway from the radio to the Internet.

VARA is a digital protocol used with Winlink.
It allows for much higher transfer rates.

PACTOR is a semi-automated data made with error correction that asks for repeats if there is interference.
The symptoms of other signals interfering with PACTOR or VARA transmissions are:
Frequent retries or timeouts
Long pauses in message transmission
Failure to establish a connection between stations
All the choices are correct

JT65, JT9, and FT8 are weak-signal digital modes.
When generating JT65, JT9 or FT8 signals using AFSK, use USB. (Upper sideband).
Hint: Mode names don't matter. RTTY uses LSB, All others use USB.

When choosing a frequency to answer an FT8 CQ, pick a clear frequency on the alternate time slot.
Unlike other modes, you do not zero-beat. FT8 decodes everything it hears. FT8 sends and receives in 15-second time slots. Pick an alternate time slot so you are transmitting when he is listening.

When using FT8 mode, computer time must be accurate within 1 second.
The decoding algorithm depends on precise timing.

Digital transmissions on the 20-meter band are from 14.070 to 14.100 MHz.
CW at the bottom of the band, SSB at the top, digital in the middle of all bands.

A common location for FT8 is from 14.074 MHz to 14.077 MHz.
FT8 is within the digital portion of the band.

The way to establish contact with a digital messaging system gateway station is to **transmit a connect message on the station's published frequency.**
Hint: Connect to contact.

PACTOR connections are limited to two stations.
To join a contact between two stations using PACTOR protocol is not possible.
The trick question asks you how to join a contact, and the answer is, "You can't."

The primary purpose of an Amateur Radio Emergency Data Network (AREDN) mesh network is to provide high-speed data services during an emergency or community event.
Hint: Emergency data network is used in emergencies.

SUMMARY: OPERATING PROCEDURES

GROUP A – PHONE OPERATING

SSB means one sideband is transmitted.

Voice mode most commonly used is single sideband.

SSB advantage is less bandwidth and greater power efficiency.

Voice communication on 160, 75 and 40 meters use lower sideband. Because it is commonly accepted.

On 12, 14 and 17 MHz, VHF/UHF use upper sideband.

To break in, say your call sign.

VOX allows hands-free operation.

CQ DX from a US station means only stations outside the lower 48 should reply.

For proper ALC action, adjust the transmit audio or microphone gain.

GROUP B – BAND PLANS, EMERGENCIES, RACES

Except during emergencies, no amateur station has priority access to a frequency.

Acknowledge a station in distress and determine what help is needed.

Interference should be resolved in a mutually acceptable manner.

Before calling CW, avoid interference by sending QRL? on CW or asking on phone.

Minimum separation on CW is 150 Hz.

Minimum separation on SSB is 3 kHz.

Follow the voluntary band plans.

50.1 to 50.125 MHz for contacts not within the 48 states.

A RACES control operator must hold an amateur license.

RACES may conduct training drills no more than one hour per week without special authorization.

Nets should have a backup plan.

GROUP C – CW OPERATING, Q SIGNALS, BREAK-IN

Full break in (QSK) can receive between code characters.

QRS: Send slower.

KN: Specific station only

QRL?: Are you busy? Or, is the frequency in use?

QSL: Received and understood.

QRN: Troubled by static

QRV: Ready to receive messages.

AR: End of a formal CW message.

"C" with a signal report means the signal has chirp.

Answer a Morse code CQ no faster than it was sent.

Zero beat is matching the transmit frequency.

GROUP D – VOLUNTEER MONITORING PROGRAM, HF OPERATIONS

Volunteer Monitoring Program monitors for rules violations.

To encourage operators to self-regulate.

Compare beam headings to locate a station.

Azimuthal map shows bearings and distances.

CQ a few times, identify, listen.

Long-path is 180 degrees from short-path.

NATO phonetics include Alpha and Delta.

Keep a log in case the FCC request information.

When in a contest, identify per normal FCC regulations.

QRP is low power.

Exchange signal reports to allow each station is operate according to conditions.

GROUP E – DIGITAL MODE OPERATING.

AFSK RTTY uses lower sideband.

Reasons you can't decode RTTY are: reversed mark and space, wrong baud rate, and wrong sideband.

Winlink is: amateur network to send and receive email on the Internet, a form of Packet Radio, and a wireless network.

A Winlink Remote Message Server is a gateway.

VARA is a digital protocol used with Winlink.

JT65, JT9 or FT8 signals with AFSK use USB. RTTY is LSB, everything else is USB.

Answer FT8 by picking a clear frequency on the alternate time slot.

FT8 computer time must be accurate within 1 second.

Digital transmissions on 20 meters between 14.070 and 14.100 MHz.

FT8 on 14.074 to 14.077 MHz.

Establish contact by transmitting a connect message.

Monitor to determine if a PACTOR channel is in use.

You cannot join a contact between 2 PACTOR stations.

An AREDN mesh network is to provide high-speed data services during an emergency or community event.

G3 - RADIO WAVE PROPAGATION

G3A – Sunspots and solar radiation; geomagnetic field and stability indices indices

Propagation is the term used to describe the distribution of radio waves. Sunspot activity affects propagation when solar radiation stimulates the ionosphere, creating clouds of charged particles called "ions." HF signals may bounce off the ionosphere and return to Earth in a phenomenon called "skip." Sometimes, the signals will bounce (refract) off the ionosphere back to Earth, back to the ionosphere, and back to the Earth again for "multi-hop" propagation. Signals can travel great distances in this manner.

Higher sunspot numbers affect HF propagation as they support a greater probability of good propagation at higher frequencies.
Hint: Sunspots are good for HF propagation.

A solar flare causes a Sudden Ionospheric Disturbance (SID), leading to a sudden increase in radio-wave absorption, most severe in the lower frequency ranges.
A Sudden Ionospheric Disturbance disrupts signals on lower frequencies more than higher frequencies.

Increased ultraviolet and X-ray radiation from solar flares affect radio propagation in approximately 8 minutes.
Hint: X-rays travel at the speed of light and take 8 minutes to arrive on Earth.

Particles travel much slower than X-rays. The X-rays serve as an early warning of what is coming in one or two days.

PROPAGATION

Charged particles from a coronal mass ejection affect radio propagation in 15 hours to several days.

Charged particles that reach Earth from solar coronal holes disturb HF communication.
Hint: Do not worry about where they came from; charged particles disturb HF.

In periods of low solar activity, 15 meters, 12 meters, and 10 meters are the least reliable for long-distance communications.
Hint: High-frequency bands need high solar activity. These higher frequencies (shorter wavelengths) would be the least reliable during low solar activity.

The solar flux index is a measure of solar radiation at 10.7 centimeters wavelength.
Hint: Solar flux is solar radiation. Don't worry about the wavelength.

A geomagnetic storm is a temporary disturbance in the Earth's geomagnetic field .
Hint: Geomagnetic storm causes a disturbance.

Earth's magnetic poles attract magnetic particles. High latitudes are near the poles, so they are affected by a geomagnetic storm.
A geomagnetic storm will degrade high-latitude HF propagation.

High geomagnetic activity can create auroras.
A benefit of high geomagnetic activity is auroras that can reflect VHF signals.
Hint: not good for HF but good for VHF.

The sun rotates every 28 days, so the same sunspots come back around.
Propagation varies in a 28-day cycle because of the sun's rotation on its axis.

The A-index indicates long-term stability of Earth's geomagnetic field.
Hint "A" = average or long term.

The K-index is the short-term stability of Earth's geomagnetic field.
Hint: Short-term, the opposite of the A, long-term, index.

20 meters is the money band.
The 20-meter band usually supports worldwide propagation during daylight hours at any point in the solar cycle.

G3B – Maximum Usable Frequency; Lowest Useable Frequency; short path and long path propagation; determining propagation conditions; ionospheric refraction

Signals can travel around the world both short path (most direct) and long path (the long way around the globe). The long path signal would take slightly longer to reach you and sound like an echo.
A characteristic of skywave signals arriving by both short and long-path are a slightly delayed echo.

Higher HF frequencies are quieter and suffer less attenuation from absorption.
The MUF is the Maximum Usable Frequency for communication between two points.

The frequency with the lowest attenuation for long-distance skip operation would be just below the MUF.
Hint: Just below the maximum usable frequency. Close to, but not over, the top.

PROPAGATION

The reverse beacon network listens and lists signal reports on the Internet.
A reliable way to determine current propagation is to use a network of automated receiving stations on the Internet to see where your transmissions are being received.

The factors affecting the MUF include:
Path distance and location
Time of day and season
Solar radiation and ionospheric disturbances
All these choices are correct.
Hint: Many things affect the MUF.

The LUF is the Lowest Usable Frequency for communication between two points.

When radio waves are below the LUF, they are attenuated before reaching the destination.
Hint: The frequency is below usable.

"Refracted back to Earth" is the phenomenon known as "skip" and supports worldwide communication.
When radio waves are below the MUF and above the LUF, they are refracted (bent) back to Earth.
Hint: Below the max and above the minimum is the sweet spot

If the LUF exceeds the MUF, no HF frequency will support communication over the path.
Hint: The floor is higher than the ceiling.

Summer thunderstorms create static and noise heard over thousands of miles. QRN!
During the summer, lower HF frequencies typically have high levels of atmospheric noise or static.

G3C – Ionospheric layers; critical angle and frequency; HF scatter, Near Vertical Incidence Skywave (NVIS)

The ionosphere consists of layers of charged ion clouds divided into the D, E, F1, and F2 regions.
The ionospheric region closest to the surface of the Earth is the D region.
Hint: D is Down low.

The D region absorbs HF but goes away at night. Then, you can hear long-distance signals.
Long distance communication on the 40-meter, 60-meter, 80-meter, and 160-meter bands are more difficult during the day because the D region absorbs signals at these frequencies during the day.

The ionospheric region most absorbent of signals below 10 MHz during daylight hours is the D layer.
Hint: Forget the over-complicated questions and remember, "The Darned D region absorbs signals."

The "critical frequency" at a given incidence angle is the highest frequency refracted back to Earth.
A higher frequency would pass through the ionosphere.

The F2 region is mainly responsible for long-distance propagation because it is the highest ionospheric region.
The higher the region, the further a bounce travels.

The maximum distance from one hop using the F2 region is 2,500 miles.
Hint: F as in twenty-Five.

PROPAGATION

The maximum distance from one hop using the E region is 1,200 miles.
Hint: E as in twelvE.

The "critical angle" is the highest takeoff angle that will return a radio wave to earth.
If the angle is steeper than the critical angle, the signal will pass through the ionosphere and out into space. If the angle is lower, the signal bounces. Vertical antennas have low takeoff angles and favor long distances.

A signal bouncing (refracting) off the ionosphere will come back down at a distance. The area the signal skips over is called the skip zone. Some signal may bounce back and is called "scatter."
The propagation that allows signals to be heard in the skip zone is called "scatter."

Scatter signals have a fluttering sound.
Multi-path reception causes the flutter.

Signals in the skip zone are usually weak because only a small part of the energy is scattered into the skip zone.

Scatter signals often sound distorted because energy is scattered into the skip zones through several different radio wave paths.
Hint: Multipath distortion.

Near Vertical Incidence Skywave (NVIS) propagation is short distance propagation using high elevation angles.
A very low antenna causes the signal to reflect off the Earth's surface and go up at a steep angle. It bounces down reasonably close to the source.

SUMMARY: PROPAGATION

GROUP A – SUNSPOTS, GEOMAGNETIC FIELD

Higher sunspot numbers mean good propagation at higher frequencies (shorter wavelengths).

Sudden Ionospheric Disturbance disrupts lower frequencies.

X-Ray and ultraviolet radiation from a solar flare arrives in 8 minutes.

Charged particles take 15 hours to several days.

Charged particles from coronal holes disturb HF communications.

Low solar activity makes 15, 12 and 10 meters least reliable.

Solar flux is a measure of solar radiation.

A geomagnetic storm is a disturbance of the geomagnetic field.

A geomagnetic storm will degrade high-latitude HF propagation.

A benefit of geomagnetic activity is auroras which reflect VHF signals.

Propagation has a 28-day cycle due to sun's rotation.

A Index is long-term stability.

K Index is short-term stability.

20 meters supports worldwide propagation.

GROUP B – MUF/LUF, SHORT-PATH, DETERMINING CONDITIONS

Short and long-path signals create an echo.

MUF is maximum usable frequency.

Frequency with the least attenuation is just below the MUF.

Use automated receiving stations to see where you are being heard.

Factors affecting MUF are: path distance and location, time of day, solar radiation and disturbances.

PROPAGATION

LUF is lowest usable frequency.

Below the LUF signals are attenuated.

Below the MUF and above the LUF, signals refract back to Earth.

If LUF exceeds MUF, nothing gets through.

Lower HF frequencies experience summer static.

GROUP C – IONOSPHERIC LAYERS, CRITICAL ANGLE AND FREQUENCY, NVIS

D region is closest to Earth.

D region absorbs signals during the day.

Critical frequency is the highest frequency refracted back to Earth.

F2 region is responsible for long distance propagation because it is the highest.

Maximum distance for one hop F2 region is 2500 miles.

Maximum distance for one hop E region is 1200 miles.

Critical angle is the highest takeoff angle that will return a radio wave to Earth.

Propagation that allows signals in the skip zone is "scatter."

Scatter signals have a fluttering sound.

Scatter signals are weak because only a small part is scattered into the skip zone.

Scatter signals sound distorted because the energy is scattered through several different paths.

NVIS is short distance communication using high elevation angles.

G4 – AMATEUR RADIO PRACTICES

G4A – Station configuration and operation

A carrier is a steady tone, perhaps someone tuning up. The notch filter "notches" or reduces it.
A "notch filter" reduces interference from carriers in the receiver passband.
Hint: Notch = reduce.

You can listen to a CW signal above or below the carrier frequency and hear the same tone. If there is interference on one side, avoid it by switching to the other side.
The advantage of selecting the opposite or "reverse" sideband when receiving CW signals is it may be possible to reduce or eliminate interference.
Hint: It might be less crowded walking on the other side of the street.

Noise blankers work on impulse noise like spark plugs or electric fences.
A noise blanker reduces receiver gain during a noise pulse.
Hint: It blanks noises by turning down the volume.

Amateur radio amplifiers using vacuum tubes are still popular and can handle a greater mismatch to an antenna system than solid state. You can tune a tube amplifier to match the antenna system.

The plate current reading of a tube amplifier that indicates the correct setting of the TUNE control is a pronounced dip.
Hint: Dip the plate.

The correct load control adjustment on a tube amplifier is desired power output without exceeding maximum allowable plate current.
Hint: The correct adjustment is desired output.

Relays act as switches when transitioning from receive to transmit. A slight delay gives the relays time to change and prevents hot-switching.
The reason to delay RF output after activating a transmitter's keying line is to allow time for the amplifier to switch from receive to transmit.

An ALC circuit automatically throttles back the drive power to prevent overload and distortion.
The reason to use Automatic Level Control (ALC) with an amplifier is to prevent excessive drive.

The ALC system should be inactive when transmitting AFSK data signals because too much ALC action distorts the signal.
Hint: Ignore the over-complicated question and remember that too much ALC action distorts the signal.

An antenna tuner matches the load with the transmitter, so maximum power transfers.
The purpose of an antenna tuner is to increase power transfer from the transmitter to the feed line.

The purpose of an electronic keyer is automatic transmission of dots and dashes for CW operation.

Noise reduction works on overall noise, atmospheric noise or noise from electrical equipment.
As the noise reduction control level is increased, received signals may become distorted.
Hint: Too much signal processing can introduce distortion.

In split mode, set the transceiver to different transmit and receive frequencies. Repeaters operate in split mode. On HF, DX stations may transmit and listen on different frequencies to reduce interference to their transmit signal.
A dual VFO on a transceiver would allow you to monitor two different frequencies.
You listen to the DX on his transmit frequency and listen to the stations calling him on his receiver frequency.

Strong signals can overwhelm the receiver causing distortion.
The attenuator function prevents signal overload from strong incoming signals.
Hint: An attenuator attenuates or reduces overload.

G4B – Tests and test equipment

An oscilloscope looks like a TV screen and displays horizontal and vertical wave patterns.
You find horizontal and vertical channel amplifiers in an oscilloscope.

An advantage of an oscilloscope versus a digital voltmeter is you can measure complex waveforms.
A digital voltmeter cannot keep up and would display wildly fluctuating numbers.

The best instrument to check the keying waveform of a CW transmitter is an oscilloscope.
Hint: You can see the wave on the screen.

To check the RF envelope pattern, connect attenuated RF output of the transmitter to the vertical input.
Hint: Too complicated! Remember: connect the transmitter's RF output to see the RF pattern.

A high-impedance voltmeter has a high resistance and therefore decreases the loading on the circuits being measured.
The high impedance means very little current flows through the meter.
Hint: The high-impedance voltmeter measures without being a drag on the circuit.

An analog meter uses a swinging needle on a scale.
An advantage of a digital, as opposed to an analog voltmeter, is higher precision.
Hint: It is easier to read 3.375 volts in digits than to see it on a scale.

Analog readout may be preferred over digital readout when adjusting for maximum or minimum values.
Hint: Easier to see a peak or dip with a swinging needle than fluctuating digits.

A two-tone test measures linearity.
A two-tone test uses two non-harmonically related audio signals.
The two signals are mixed and fed to the transmitter. An oscilloscope shows any distortion.

A directional wattmeter can determine the standing wave ratio.
Hint: The meter is directional, so it measures forward and reflected power from which you calculate SWR.

An antenna analyzer can measure the impedance of coaxial cable.

Connect the antenna and feed line to an antenna analyzer to measure SWR.
Hint: You are using an antenna analyzer. Connect the antenna and feed line.

When making measurements with an antenna analyzer, strong signals from a nearby transmitter can affect the accuracy.
The analyzer assumes the transmitter's signals are power reflected from the antenna, which throws off the readings.

G4C – Interference to consumer electronics; grounding and bonding

A capacitor passes high frequencies. A bypass capacitor will act as an RF short-circuit across the audio device.
To reduce RF interference to audio frequency devices, use a bypass capacitor.

Sparks produce broadband noise.
Interference over a wide range of frequencies could be caused by arcing at a poor electrical connection.

An audio device experiencing RF interference from a single-sideband phone transmitter would produce distorted speech.
The device does not have a circuit to decode single sideband audio, so the speech sounds distorted.

RF interference from a CW transmitter would sound like on-and-off clicking or humming.
The device does not have a circuit to decode CW tones either.
Hint: It is CW, so the sound would be on-and-off like Morse code.

Impedance is resistance to alternating current.
A cause of high voltages that produce RF burns is the ground wire has a high impedance at that frequency.
The ground wire is not conducting the RF away. The current is staying on the radio chassis.

Hint: There is no such thing as a "resonant ground rod." A ground rod is the metal stake you pound in the ground. The answer has to be "the ground wire has high impedance."

A resonant ground connection can cause high RF voltages on the enclosures of station equipment. Change the ground wire length.

Don't use soldered joints in lightning protection ground connections because the heat of a lightning strike will likely destroy the soldered joint.
Hint: Simplify the over-complicated question: heat melts solder.

A bypass capacitor bypasses RF to ground, and a choke impedes RF. Both are effective.
Reduce RF interference caused by common-mode current on an audio cable by placing a ferrite choke on the cable.
Hint: The ferrite choke chokes off the RF on the cable.

A ground loop occurs when there are multiple paths for electric currents flowing to ground. Multiple paths could have different resistance to ground which would support different voltages among the equipment. The different voltages cause current to pass, bringing hum and buzz.
A symptom of a ground loop would be hum on your signal.

"Bonding" is tying all the equipment enclosures together, so there is no difference in potential among them.
To avoid a ground loop, bond equipment enclosures together.
To minimize RF "hot spots," bond all equipment enclosures together.

Hint: If you bond everything together, there cannot be any spots hotter than others. Look for "bond" in the answer.

The metal enclosure of every item of station equipment should be grounded to ensure hazardous voltages cannot appear on the chassis.
If a high voltage were on the chassis, it would drain to ground, probably blowing a fuse. Better blow a fuse than have the voltage drain through you.

G4D – Speech processors; S Meters; sideband operation near band edges

A speech processor boosts the low-volume parts of the audio, making the average power higher.
The purpose of a speech processor is to increase the apparent loudness of transmitted voice signals.
Hint: Increasing apparent loudness is good.

A speech processor affects the transmitted signal by increasing average power.

An incorrectly adjusted speech processor can result in:
Distorted speech
Excessive intermodulation products
Excessive background pickup.
All these choices are correct.
Hint: Incorrect adjustment can lead to distortion and excess so all these choices are correct.

An S meter measures the received signal strength.
*Hint: *S*trength meter.*

The change in signal strength represented by one S unit is 6 dB.

An S meter reads signal strength from 1-9 and then by decibels above S9. Decibels are logarithmic, based on a power of 10.
A signal that reads 20 dB over S9 compared to one that reads S9 is 20 dB stronger, and that is 100 times more powerful.
Add or subtract decibels to get an answer. 10 dB is ten times, and another 10 dB is ten times that = 100 times more powerful.

A two-times increase in power is 3 dB. Each S-unit is 6 dB. 3 dB is double the power and equals about one-half S-unit. To increase a full S-unit, you need to double the power and double it again to improve 6 dB.
To go from S8 to S9, you need to increase your power 4 times

To go from 100 watts to 200 watts to 400 watts would be 6 dB or 1 S-unit. Doubling again to 800 watts would only add a 1/2 S-unit. 1500 watts is another 1/2 S unit. That is why you will hear it said, "The first 400 watts are the most important." A 1500-watt amplifier is much more expensive and creates a lot of strain on your antenna and coax. A 400-watt amplifier is more manageable and cost-effective.

Don't operate too close to the band edge, or your signal might be over the edge. The frequency displayed on your radio is the carrier frequency, and your signal will be above (Upper Sideband) or below (Lower Sideband) the carrier frequency.

The frequency range occupied by a 3 kHz LSB signal when the displayed frequency is 7.178 MHz would be 7.175 to 7.178 MHz.
The stated frequency is in MHz (millions). That last digit is thousands. It is lower sideband, so the signal is below the carrier frequency. 7.178 MHz is the carrier frequency. Subtract 3 from the last digit (3 kHz) to get the lowest end of the signal.

The frequency range occupied by a 3 kHz USB signal when the displayed frequency is 14.347 MHz would be 14.347 to 14.350 MHz.
This time, it is upper sideband, so the signal is all above the carrier frequency. Add 3 to the last digit.

How close to the lower edge of the band should your displayed carrier frequency be when using 3kHz wide LSB? 3 kHz above the band edge.
All the signal is on the lower side of the carrier frequency. At the lower edge of the band, the carrier has to be at least 3 kHz up to keep all the signal within the band.

How close to the upper edge of the band should your displayed carrier frequency be when using 3 kHz wide USB? The displayed frequency should be 3 kHz below the band edge.
All the signal is on the upper side of the carrier frequency, so the carrier must be at least 3 kHz down to keep your entire signal within the band.

G4E – HF mobile radio installations; alternative energy source operation

A capacitance hat looks like spokes on the vertical part of the antenna and makes it electrically longer.
A capacitance hat on a mobile antenna serves to electrically lengthen a physically short antenna.

A corona ball on an HF mobile antenna reduces high voltage discharge from the tip of the antenna.
A small sharp tip can throw off energy-wasting sparks. The ball blunts the tip.

Wiring directly to the battery with heavy wire provides maximum power to a mobile installation.
A direct fused power connection would be best for a 100-watt mobile installation if it goes to the battery using heavy-gauge wire.
Hint: Too much information! Connect to the battery with heavy gauge wire.

Don't draw power for a 100-watt HF transceiver from the vehicle's auxiliary power socket because the socket's wiring may be inadequate for the current drawn by the transceiver.
Cigarette lighter sockets cannot handle much power. Heavy wire connected directly to the battery is best. A direct connection also isolates the power source, preventing interference to or from other systems in the car.

The following may cause interference on an HF radio installed in a vehicle:
Battery charging system
Fuel delivery system,
Vehicle control computer.
All these choices are correct.
Hint: Car electronics can cause interference, so all choices are correct.

The most limiting factor in an HF mobile installation is the efficiency of an electrically short antenna.
A full-size quarter-wave 20-meter antenna would be 1/4 of 20 meters or about 16 feet tall! That is much larger than practical for a vehicle.

We can use various designs to shorten the antenna (like capacity hats and coils).
The disadvantage of a shortened antenna is that its operating bandwidth may be very limited.
That means you can only operate a small range of

frequencies before it needs additional tuning. A short antenna is also less efficient than full-size.

The process by which sunlight is changed into electricity is called photovoltaic conversion.
A fully illuminated photovoltaic cell produces .5 VDC (Volts Direct Current).

Many cells chained together provide the required voltage and current, series to boost the voltage and parallel to increase current capacity.
Cells are connected in a series-parallel configuration.

A series diode connected between the solar panel and a storage battery prevents self-discharge of the battery during times of low or no illumination.
The diode lets current flow only one way–into the battery, not out of the battery through the panels.

When connecting a solar panel to a lithium iron phosphate battery, the panel must have a charge controller.
Hint: The charger controls charging.

SUMMARY: AMATEUR RADIO PRACTICES

GROUP A – STATION CONFIGURATION AND OPERATION

A notch filter notches out interference.

Using the reverse sideband on CW may reduce interference.

A noise blanker reduces gain during a noise pulse.

To tune a tube amplifier, dip the plate.

Increase the load control to desired output without exceeding the maximum plate current.

Delay the RF output when switching from receive to transmit to allow time for switching.

Use ALC to prevent excessive drive.

ALC should be inactive when transmitting data signals to prevent distortion.

An antenna tuner increases the power transfer from transmitter to the feed line.

An automatic keyer generates CW dots and dashes.

Increasing the noise reduction control may cause distortion on the received signals.

A dual VFO transceiver allows you to monitor two frequencies.

The attenuator function prevents signal overload.

GROUP B – TESTS AND TEST EQUIPMENT

An oscilloscope has horizontal and vertical amplifiers.

An oscilloscope can measure complex waveforms.

Check the keying waveform with an oscilloscope.

To check the RF envelope pattern, connected the transmitter RF output to the vertical input.

A high-impedance voltmeter decreases loading on the measured circuits.

Digital voltmeters have higher precision than analog.

Analog meters are preferred when adjusting for maximum or minimum values.

A two-tone test measures linearity.

A two-tone test uses two non-harmonically related audio signals.

A directional wattmeter can determine the SWR.

An antenna analyzer can measure the impedance of coaxial cable.

Connect the antenna and feed line to an antenna analyzer to measure SWR.

Strong nearby signals can affect the accuracy of an antenna analyzer.

GROUP C – INTERFERENCE, GROUNDING AND BONDING

Use a bypass capacitor to reduce RF interference.

Interference over a wide range of frequencies could be caused by electrical arcing.

SSB interference sounds like distorted speech.

CW interference sounds like on-and-off clicking or humming.

RF burns occur when the ground wire has a high impedance at that frequency.

A resonant ground connection can cause high RF voltages on equipment enclosures.

Lightning can melt soldered joints.

Reduce RF interference with ferrite chokes.

A ground loop sounds like hum or buzz on your signal.

To avoid a ground loop, bond equipment enclosures together.

To minimize hot spots, bond all equipment enclosures together.

Ground equipment enclosures to ensure hazardous voltages cannot appear on the chassis.

GROUP D – SPEECH PROCESSORS, S METEERS BAND EDGES

A speech processor increases the apparent loudness of transmitted voice signals.

It does so by increasing average power.

An incorrectly adjusted speech processor can result in:

distorted speech, excessive intermodulation products and excessive background pickup.

An S meter measures signal strength.

One S unit is 6 dB.

A signal 20 dB over S9 is 20 dB or 100 times stronger.

To go from S8 to S9 requires a 6dB increase.

If the carrier is at 7.178 MHz, a 3 kHz LSB signal would be from 7.175 to 7.178 MHz.

If the carrier is at 14.347 MHz, a 3 kHz USB signal would go from 14.347 to 14.350 MHz.

Using 3 kHz wide LSB, the carrier should be 3 kHz above the band edge.

Using 3 kHz wide USB, the carrier should be 3 kHz below the band edge.

GROUP E – MOBILE INSTALLATION, ALTERNATIVE ENERGY

A capacitance hat electrically lengthens an antenna.

A corona ball reduces high voltage discharge.

Direct fused power connection goes directly to battery.

A vehicle's auxiliary power socket may be inadequate for the transceiver's current draw.

Limiting factor in HF mobile installation is efficiency of a short antenna.

Disadvantage of a short antenna is narrow bandwidth.

The battery charging system, fuel delivery system, and vehicle control computer may cause interference in a vehicle installation.

Fully illuminated photovoltaic cell produces .5 volts.

Cells are connected in series-parallel.

Series diode prevents solar panel self-discharge.

A lithium iron phosphate battery must have a charge controller.

G5 – ELECTRICAL PRINCIPLES

G5A – Reactance; inductance; capacitance, impedance; impedance transformation; resonance

Reactance is opposition to the flow of an alternating current caused by capacitance of inductance.
Hint: Too complicated! Reactance is opposition to alternating current.

Opposition to the flow of alternating current in an inductor is called reactance.
Opposition to the flow of alternating current in a capacitor is called reactance.

Reactance is measured in ohms.
Ohms – the same measurement as resistance, but "resistance" refers to opposition to direct current.

The letter representing reactance is X.
Hint: X marks the spot.

An inductor reacts to AC as the frequency of the AC increases, the reactance increases.
Inductors block AC. Higher frequency = more effect.

A capacitor reacts to AC as the frequency of the AC increases, the reactance decreases.
Capacitors pass AC. Higher frequency = less effect.

Reactance in an inductor goes up with frequency while in a capacitor, reactance goes down. Where they cross is resonance.
In an LC circuit[9] at resonance, inductive reactance and capacitive reactance cancel.

---

[9] An LC circuit has an inductor (L) and capacitor (C).

When capacitive and inductive reactance are equal in a series LC circuit, resonance causes impedance to be very low.
Hint: They exhibit opposite effects and cancel.

Impedance is the ratio of voltage to current.
The same as Ohm's law, R=E/I.

The reverse of impedance is called admittance.
Hint: It doesn't impede, it admits.

When the impedance of an electrical load is equal to the impedance of the power source, the source can deliver maximum power to the load. We call that "matching."

Devices used for impedance matching include a:
Transformer
Pi-network
Length of the transmission line.
All these choices are correct.
Hint: Many devices are available for impedance matching, so all these choices are correct.

G5B – The decibel; current and voltage dividers; electrical power calculations; sine wave root-mean-square (RMS) values; PEP calculations

Decibels are logarithmic (power of 10).
The dB change that represents a factor of two increase or decrease in power is 3dB.
Remember the S meter question: double your power to add 3 dB. Double it again to add 6 dB or one S-unit.

A power loss of 1 dB would be about 20.6 percent.
Hint: Memorize this one.

Components connected in series are end-to-end. In parallel, they are next to each other.
In a purely resistive parallel circuit, the total current is the sum of the currents through each branch.
Hint: The total current has to equal the sum of all the branches. "Total" is a "sum."

Ohm's law and the magic circles were on the Technician test. Solve by covering up the "answer" and applying the remaining formula. E= volts, I=amperes, R=resistance and P=Power.

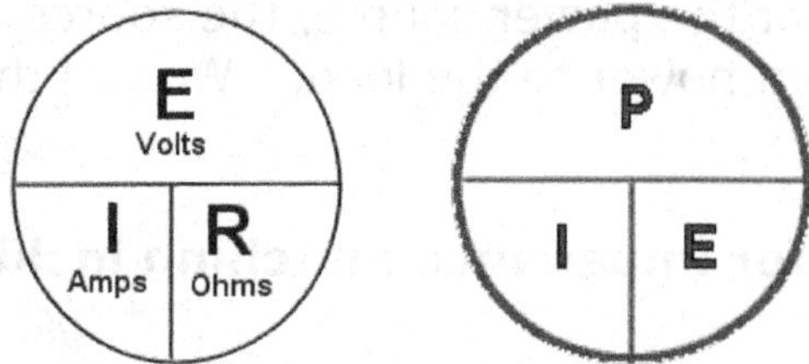

On the General test, we mix the two circles to solve more complex power problems. Write the circles and formulas on the back of the answer sheet when you first sit down, and you won't forget them.

Substituting the I in our equation: $P=E^2/R$.
Substitute the E and $P=I^2R$.
That upraised 2 means the number is squared or multiplied by itself.

Two formulas to remember:
Power equals voltage squared <u>divided</u> by the resistance. $P=E^2/R$**.**
Power equals current squared <u>times</u> the resistance. $P=I^2R$**.**

400 volts DC into an 800 ohm load will use 200 watts.
Solve: $P=E^2/R$*.* $P = 400 \times 400 / 800 = 200$ *watts.*

A 12 VDC light bulb that draws .2 amperes uses 2.4 watts.
Solve: P=IE. P = .2 x 12 = 2.4 watts. "VDC" means volts of direct current.

7 milliamperes flowing through 1250 ohms resistance will use 61 milliwatts.
Solve: $P=I^2R$ *P = .007 x .007 x 1250 = .061 watts or 61 milliwatts. Watch your decimal points or cheat and figure milliamperes must be milliwatts.*

AC power measurements present a challenge because the voltage and current vary throughout the cycle. How do you find the equivalent in DC?
The value of an AC signal that produces the same power dissipation in a resistor as a DC voltage of the same value is called the RMS value.
Hint: You don't care how it is measured; AC to DC conversion is RMS.

RMS stands for Root Mean Square. It is a way of averaging the measurements over the waveform.

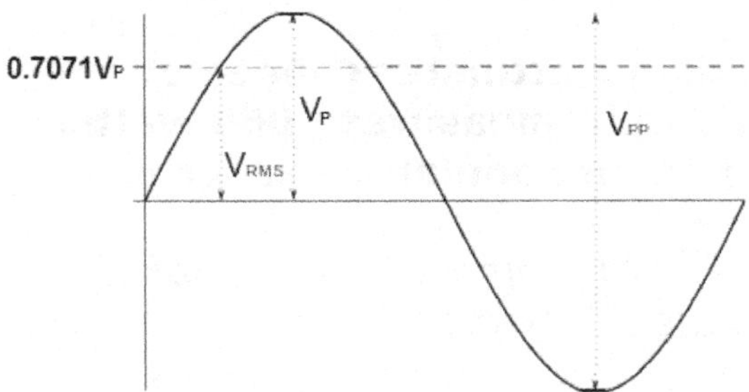

The RMS voltage of a simple sine wave, as you see above, is .7071 x the peak voltage. Round it off to .707.
The RMS voltage of a sine wave with a value of 17 volts peak is 12 volts.
Solve: Peak x .707 = RMS. *17 x .707 = 12.*

Solving in the other direction, RMS / .707 = peak voltage. Caution: That is peak voltage (Vp in the chart). Peak-to-peak AC voltage (Vpp in the chart) would be twice that. To convert peak-to-peak to peak, we divide the peak-to-peak voltage by 2 and vice-versa. Then we use our familiar DC Ohm's law equations.

The peak-to-peak voltage of a sine wave with an RMS voltage of 120 volts would be 339.4 volts.
Solve: RMS / .707 = peak. 120 / .707 = 169.7 volts peak. The question asks for peak-to-peak voltage, so multiply that by 2 = 339.4 volts.

The RMS voltage across a 50-ohm dummy load dissipating 1200 watts would be 245 volts.
The voltage is in RMS, so we do not have to convert to use our familiar Ohms law equations. We know the power, and we know ohms.
Solve for volts: $P=E^2/R$. $1200 = E^2/50$. *Multiply both sides by 50 to give* $60000 = E^2$, *and the square root of 60000 is 245 volts.*

PEP is Peak Envelope Power. If the signal is not modulated, the peak power and average power will be the same.
If an average reading wattmeter connected to the transmitter's output measures 1060 watts, the output PEP of an unmodulated carrier is also 1060 watts.
Hint: Watch for the word "unmodulated." That tells you the PEP equals the average.

If the output from a transmitter measures 500 volts peak-to-peak and the load is 50 ohms, the output is 625 watts.
Solve: Divide peak-to-peak by 2 (250) and multiply that by .707 to get RMS (176.75). $P=E^2 / R$. *Square 176.75 (31,240) and divide by 50 = 625 watts.*

The output PEP produced by 200 volts peak-to-peak across a 50-ohm dummy load is 100 watts.

Solve: Divide peak-to-peak by two to find the peak voltage. Convert peak to RMS by multiplying by .707. Then apply $P=E^2/R$.

Hint: Fear not! You will only get one question from this section and if you miss, you can still miss 8 more questions from other sections and pass.

G5C – RESISTORS, CAPACITORS, AND INDUCTORS IN SERIES AND PARALLEL; TRANSFORMERS

Transformers comprise two or more wire coils and work their magic because of mutual inductance between the coils. The alternating current in one coil induces current to the other. The ratio of turns determines whether the voltage steps up or down and by what amount.

Voltage appears across the secondary winding of a transformer when an AC voltage source is connected across the primary winding because of mutual inductance.
Hint: Transformers have coils of wire, so it is inductance, "mutual inductance."

Apply power to the primary side and derive power from the secondary side. The voltage ratio is the ratio of the number of turns. If there are fewer turns on the secondary side, the voltage will be less, and the transformer is "step-down."

If you apply voltage to the secondary winding of a 4:1 voltage step-down transformer instead of the primary winding, the input voltage is multiplied by 4.
Reversing the windings reverses the effect and makes it a step-up transformer at the same ratio, 4:1.

The voltage output of a transformer with a 500-turn primary and 1500-turn secondary when 120 VAC is applied to the primary could be 360 volts.
Hint: Secondary has more turns, so it is step up. Amount is the ratio of the number of turns.
Solve: 1500 / 500 = 3 turns ratio. 3 X 120 = 360 volts.

Ohm's law says increasing the voltage in the secondary has got to be doing something with the amperage. It takes more amperes in the primary to generate the energy needed to step up the voltage in the secondary.
The primary winding of many voltage step-up transformers is larger in diameter than the conductor of the secondary winding to accommodate the higher current of the primary.

Transformers can also transform impedance loads, but the formula is more complicated. The ratio of wire turns is the square root of the impedance ratio.
To match a 600-ohm output impedance to a 50 ohm cable, you would want a 3.5:1 ratio of turns.
Solve: 600/50 = 12 and the square root of 12 is 3.5.
Cheat: There is only one question about transformer impedance matching. Recognize the answer is 3.5.

When we connect resistors or inductors in series (end-to-end), the current passes through one, and then the next, the total resistance or inductance is the total of all the component values in series. Here is a schematic diagram of resistors in series.

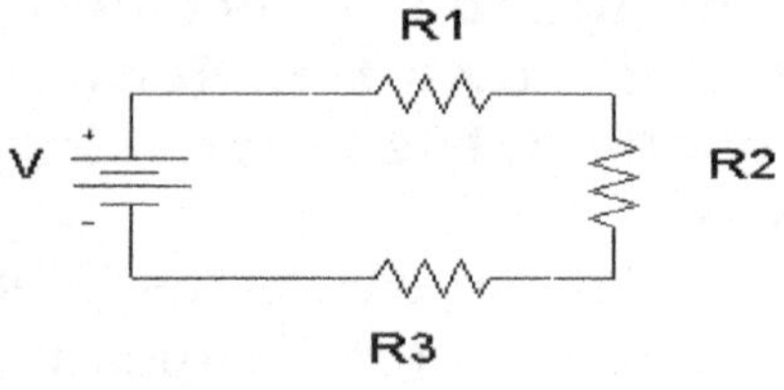

Resistors in series

A 20 millihenry inductor in series with a 50-millihenry inductor would be 70 millihenries.
Solve: Inductors or resistors in series are the sum. 20 + 50 = 70.

The component added to an inductor to increase the total inductance is an inductor in series.

When we put the resistors (or inductors) in parallel (across each other), the current is spread out and divided among them and the total resistance will be less than any individual component.
In a purely resistive parallel circuit, the total current is the sum of the currents through each branch.
Hint: The total current must equal the sum of all the branches. "Total" is a "sum."

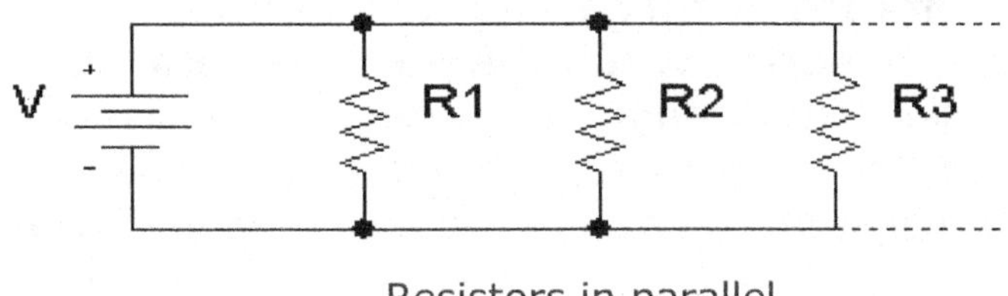

Resistors in parallel

For resistors or inductors in parallel, the total resistance follows the formula:

$$\text{Total} = \frac{1}{1/R_1 + 1/R_2 + 1/R_3}$$

Hint: First figure the values of 1/R or 1/L, then add them up and divide 1 by the result.

The total resistance of a 10 ohm, 20 ohm and 50 ohm resistor in parallel is 5.9 ohms.
Solve: Resistors in parallel. 1/10 = .1 and 1/20 = .05 and 1/50 = .02 so .1+.05+.02 = .17 and 1/.17 = 5.9 ohms.

The total resistance of a 100 and 200-ohm resistor in parallel would be 67 ohms.
Solve: Resistors in parallel. 1/100 = .01 and 1/200 = .005. Then, .01+.005 = .015 and 1/.015 =67 ohms.

Capacitors work the opposite of resistors and inductors. In parallel, capacitance increases to the sum of the components. Think of the plates in a capacitor. By lining up additional plates, in parallel, you increase the capacitance.
The component that increases the total capacitance of a capacitor is a capacitor in parallel.

Putting capacitors in series means the total capacitance decreases. They follow the same formula as resistors or inductors in parallel.

The capacitance of three 100-microfarad capacitors in series would be 33.3 microfarads.
Solve: A shortcut when all the series capacitors (or parallel inductors or resistors) are the same value is to divide the value by the number of components. 100/3 = 33.3.

Three 10-millihenry inductors in parallel would be 3.3 millihenries.
Solve: Inductors in parallel with the same values. 10 / 3 = 3.3.

Review your decimals. The picofarad (pF) is the smallest, Nanofarad (nF) is 1000 picofarads.

Two 5.0 nanofarad capacitors and one 750 picofarad capacitor in parallel would be the total of them. *Solve: First, convert the picofarads to nanofarads by dividing by 1000. 5 + 5 + .750 = 10.750 nanofarads.*
Cheat: Add the nanos (5 + 5 = 10). The answer is just a little over 10 nanos.

SUMMARY: ELECTRICAL PRINCIPALS

GROUP A REACTANCE; INDUCTANCE; CAPACITANCE; IMPEDANCE TRANSFORMATION; RESONANCE

Reactance is opposition to alternating current in an inductor or capacitor.

Reactance is measured in Ohms.

The letter representing reactance is X.

As frequency increases, reactance in an inductor increases.

As frequency increases, reactance in a capacitor decreases.

Inductive and capacitive reactances cancel.

When equal in a series circuit, resonance causes impedance to be very low.

Impedance is the ratio of voltage to current. R=E/I.

Reverse of impedance is admittance.
Impedance matching devices include transformer, Pi-network, length of transmission line.

GROUP B DECIBELS; POWER CALCULATIONS; RMS; PEP

A factor of 2 increase or decrease is 3dB.

1 dB loss is about 20.6%

Total current in a parallel circuit is the sum of the branches.

Power is current times voltage. P=IE

Power is voltage squared divided by resistance $P=E^2R$.

Power is current squared times resistance $P=I^2R$.

AC signal that produces the same power distribution as a DC voltage is RMS value.

RMS value is peak voltage times .707.

Peak voltage is half of peak-to-peak.

Unmodulated carrier power is the same as peak.

ELECTRICAL PRINCIPLES

GROUP C – RESISTORS, CAPACITORS, INDUCTORS IN SERIES AND PARALLEL; TRANSFORMERS

Transformers rely on mutual inductance.

Voltage transforms by ratio of the turns.

Fewer turns on the secondary means step down.

If you reverse a 4:1 transformer, the input voltage is multiplied by 4.

Primary winding on a step up is larger because it needs to carry more current.

Ratio of turns for matching impedances is the square root of the impedance ratio.

Inductors or resistors in series are the sum.

Add an inductor in series to increase inductance.

Inductors or resistors in parallel use the formula 1 divided by $(1/R_1 + 1/R_2 + 1/R_3)$

Capacitors in parallel are the sum.

Add an capacitor in parallel to increase capacitance.

Capacitors in series use the formula 1 divided by $(1/R_1 + 1/R_2 + 1/R_3)$

G6 – CIRCUIT COMPONENTS

G6A – Resistors; capacitor; inductors; rectifiers; solid-state diodes and transistors; vacuum tubes; batteries

BATTERIES

As a battery gets "used up," the voltage drops, which is why a flashlight dims. At some point, the voltage drops enough to damage a rechargeable battery.

The minimum allowable discharge voltage for maximum life of a 12-volt lead-acid battery is 10.5 volts.
Monitor the battery's voltage. Low voltage will also cause radio problems.

The advantage of batteries with low internal resistance is they have high discharge current.
Hint: Ohm's law: low resistance means high current.

RECTIFIERS

Rectifiers (diodes) allow current to pass in only one direction. There are various materials used to make diodes, and they have different characteristics. One difference is the junction threshold voltage which describes the minimum voltage required before the diode starts conducting.

For a conventional silicon diode, the junction threshold voltage is 0.7 volts.
Cheat: Silicon has 7 letters = .7 volts.

For a germanium diode, the junction threshold voltage is 0.3 volts.
Cheat: The other mid-range answer.

CIRCUIT COMPONENTS

RESISTORS

Most resistors are compressed carbon. Some use a coil of resistance wire, but the coil of wire can act as an inductor.
You would not want to use wire wound resistors in an RF circuit because the resistor's inductance would make the circuit performance unpredictable.

CAPACITORS

Capacitors are made of layers of conducting material separated by a non-conducting material called a "dielectric." The dielectric could be air, plastic film, ceramic, or a gel of chemicals. An electrolytic capacitor has a layer of gel.
A characteristic of an electrolytic capacitor is that it has a high capacitance for a given volume. Electrolytics pack lots of capacitance in a smaller package.

A characteristic of low-voltage ceramic capacitors is their low cost.
Cheat: Low voltage = low cost.

TRANSISTORS

Transistors can be switches or amplifiers. Saturation means it is conducting, and cutoff means it is not.
The operating points for a bipolar transistor are its saturation and cutoff.
Hint: The question has a tricky wrong answer. Remember, saturation and cutoff are points. "Active region" is the wrong answer.

A MOSFET is a Metal Oxide Semiconductor Field Effect Transistor.
The MOSFET has a gate and a channel. The gate is separated from the channel by a thin insulating layer.
Cheat: A field has a gate separated from the channel.

VACUUM TUBES

Vacuum tubes have a cathode that heats to generate electrons, a plate to catch those electrons and one or more grids between the two. Grids generate electrical fields to control the flow of electrons to the plate.

The element of a vacuum tube used to regulate the flow of electrons between cathode and plate is the control grid.
Hint: You regulate with a control.

The purpose of a screen grid is to reduce grid-to-plate capacitance.
Hint: It screens the grid from the plate.

INDUCTORS

As frequency increases, the coils of an inductor couple. The inductor acts like a capacitor, losing the ability to impede RF.
When an inductor operates above its self-resonant frequency, it becomes capacitive

G6B – Analog and digital integrated circuits (ICs); microprocessors; memory; microwave ICs (MMICs); display devices; RF connectors; ferrite cores

FERRITE CORES

To increase a coil's inductance, wrap the coil around iron or ferrite. This concentrates the magnetic field. A toroidal inductor (toroid) is a donut-shaped circle of ferrite.

Ferrite is a mixture of metal and ceramic. The mix determines performance characteristics.
The performance of a ferrite core at different frequencies is determined by the composition, or "mix," of materials used.

CIRCUIT COMPONENTS

The advantage of using a ferrite core toroidal inductor is:
Large values of inductance may be obtained
The magnetic properties can be optimized for a specific range of frequencies
Most of the magnetic field is contained in the core.
All these choices are correct.
Hint: Lots of advantages to using a toroidal inductor, so all choices are correct

A ferrite bead or core reduces common-mode RF current on the shield of a coaxial cable by creating an impedance in the current's path.
Hint: The ferrite impedes the path. It creates a choke.

INTEGRATED CIRCUITS

Integrated circuits (ICs or chips) contain many components to form complete circuits.
MMIC means Monolithic Microwave Integrated Circuit. It is an IC that operates at microwave frequencies.
Hint: Remember the odd-sounding Monolithic Microwave.

CMOS and TTL describe two types of logic ICs. CMOS is the more modern construction. It means Complementary Metal Oxide Semiconductor.
Compared to TTL, CMOS has the advantage of low power consumption.
Hint: All the answers look tempting, so memorize "low power consumption."

Analog chips do not "think," they "do." Analog devices are regulators, amplifiers, and filters.
An integrated circuit operational amplifier is analog.
Hint: An amplifier does not think; it functions.

DISPLAY DEVICES

LEDs are light-emitting diodes. They use less power and last longer than incandescent lamps.

An LED is forward biased when emitting light.
Hint: When lit, it is conducting.

An LCD is a liquid crystal display. It displays dark letters over a lighter background.
A liquid crystal display has higher contrast in high ambient lighting compared to an LED.
Hint: Dark letters over a light background gives higher contrast.

CONNECTORS

An N connector attaches coaxial cable.
The N connector is moisture resistant and useful to 10 GHz.
Hint: N = No moisture.

An SMA connector is a small threaded connector suitable for signals up to several GHz.
You often find SMAs on handheld radios.
Hint: SMA = SMALL

Connectors used for low frequency or DC signal connections on a transceiver are commonly RCA phono.
Hint: Phono means audio, which is low frequency. The other answers are all RF, high frequency.

BNC connectors feature a quick-connect twist-and-lock mechanism often found on low-power transmitters or VHF/UHF rigs.
BNC connectors have an upper frequency limit of 4 GHz.

SUMMARY: CIRCUIT COMPONENTS

GROUP A - Resistors; capacitors; inductors; rectifiers; solid state diodes; vacuum tubes; batteries

Lead acid minimum discharge voltage is 10.5 volts.

Batteries with low internal resistance may have high discharge current.

Silicon diode junction threshold voltage .7 volts.

Germanium diode junction threshold voltage .3 volts.

Inductance in a wire-wound resistor could affect the circuit.

An electrolytic capacitor has high capacitance for a given volume.

Low voltage ceramic capacitors are low-cost.

The operating points of a transistor are saturation and cut-off.

MOSFET has a gate and a channel separated by a thin insulating layer.

In a vacuum tube, a control grid regulates the flow of electrons between the cathode and plate.

A screen grid reduces grid-to-plate capacitance.

Reversing a polarized capacitor can cause the capacitor to short circuit, destroy the dielectric layer, overheat and explode.

An inductor above its self-resonant frequency becomes capacitive.

GROUP B – Ics, MMICs, display devices, RF connectors, ferrite cores

An advantage of a ferrite core is large inductance, magnetic properties to match the frequency, magnetic field contained within the core.

Performance at different frequencies determined by the mix of materials.

Ferrite bead reduces RF current by creating an impedance in its path.

MMIC is Monolithic Microwave

CMOS has lower power conception than TTL.

Integrated circuit operational amplifier is an analog device.

LED is forward biased when emitting.

Liquid crystal display has higher contrast compared to LED.

N connector is moisture resistant.

SMA connector is small threaded.

Low frequency or power connections use an RCA connector.

Upper limit of BNC connectors is 4 GHz.

G7 – PRACTICAL CIRCUITS

G7A – Power supplies; schematic symbols

POWER SUPPLIES

Inductors and capacitors form a tuned circuit or filter. **A power supply filter network uses capacitors and inductors.**
Hint: They filter the pulsating DC coming from a rectifier.

Capacitors can store dangerous amounts of energy for a long time.
A bleeder resistor discharges the filter capacitors when power is removed.
Hint: Bleeder resistors bleed off the charge.

Power supplies operate on 60-cycle AC out of the house outlet. Switchmode power supplies convert the 60-cycle AC to a higher frequency and can use a smaller and lighter transformer.
The characteristic of a switchmode power supply compared to a linear power supply is higher frequency operation allows the use of smaller components.

The portion of the AC cycle converted to DC by a half-wave rectifier is 180 degrees.
A half-wave power supply only blocks the reverse voltage.

The portion of the AC cycle converted to DC by a full-wave rectifier is 360 degrees.
Hint: A full wave is 360 degrees, half is 180.

A full-wave rectifier circuit is a combination of diodes that conducts AC in one direction and inverts the other side of the cycle, so it also appears in the same direction. Both sides of the AC are combined to go in one direction in a full-wave rectifier.

The output waveform of an unfiltered full-wave rectifier connected to a resistive load in a series of DC pulses at twice the frequency of the AC input.
Hint: See the wave forms below.

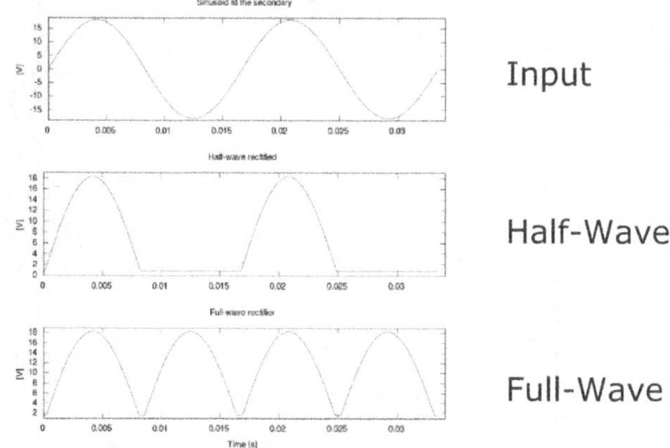

The rectifier circuit that uses two diodes and a center-tapped transformer is full-wave.
Hint: One answer is "full-wave bridge." Don't fall off the bridge.

A characteristic of a half-wave rectifier is only one diode is required.
Hint: To produce both "sides" of the alternating current requires two diodes.

SCHEMATIC SYMBOLS

These questions reference the schematic diagram on the next page. This diagram is the only schematic on the General test.

A field effect transistor is Symbol 1.

An NPN transistor is Symbol 2.

A Zener diode is Symbol 5.

A solid core transformer is Symbol 6.

A tapped inductor is Symbol 7.

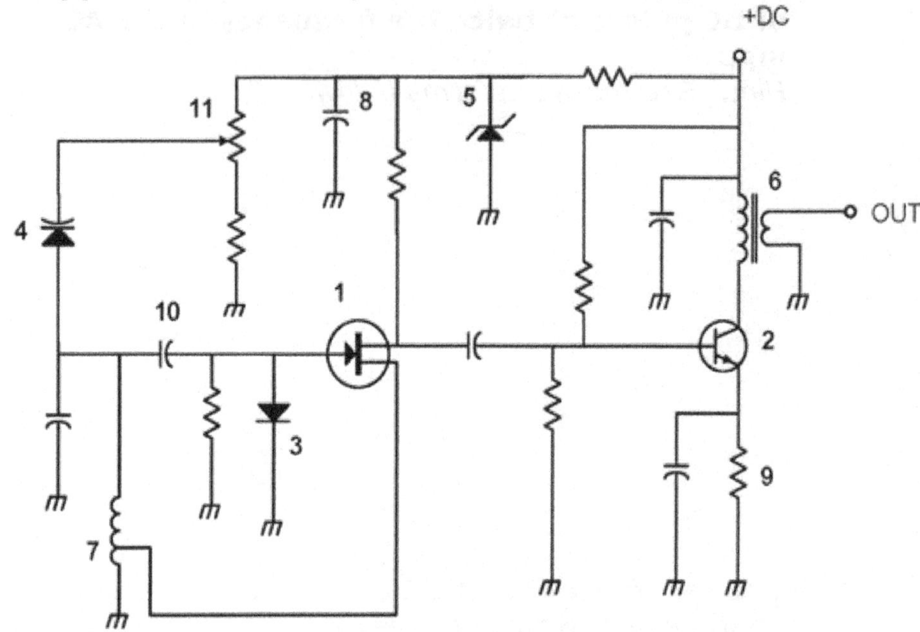

Figure G7-1

G7B – Digital circuits; amplifiers and oscillators

AMPLIFIERS

"Oscillate" means to swing back and forth on a regular cycle, and an oscillator generates an AC signal. One way to do this is through a feedback loop. The circuit acts like a dog chasing its tail, and the number of circles (cycles) in a second is the frequency in Hertz.

Amplifiers can self-oscillate; go into an uncontrolled feedback loop that destroys the amplifier. To combat an unwanted feedback loop, introduce a bit of negative feedback and cancel the loop. The process is called "neutralization."

The purpose of neutralizing an amplifier is to eliminate self-oscillation.

"Linear" means the input and output match.
A linear amplifier is an amplifier in which the output preserves the input waveform.

The efficiency of an RF power amplifier is determined by dividing the RF output by the DC input power.
If you get 100 watts of RF output with 200 watts of DC input, you are 50% efficient.
Hint: Efficiency compares what you put in (DC input) with what you get out (RF output).

Amplifier designs come in different classes. There is a trade-off between efficiency and linearity. The Class C amplifier is only active for part of the signal's cycle, so it is very efficient but is not linear.
The class with the highest efficiency is Class C.

FM is frequency modulation, and audio jiggles the transmit frequency. An FM receiver can recover the sound even though the amplifier only conducts part of a cycle.
A Class C power stage is appropriate for amplifying an FM signal.

A Class A amplifier conducts 100% of the time.
Class A is very linear but uses lots of power.

DIGITAL CIRCUITS

Digital circuits operate on binary code. All data is ones and zeros. The advantage of the binary system is binary "ones" and "zeros" are easy to represent by an "on" and "off" state.

If a binary counter has 3 bits, it has 8 states.
Each bit can be 0 or 1 so the possible combinations are 000, 001, 010, 011, 100, 101, 110 and 111. That

would be 2^3 or 2 to the third power: 2 X 2 X 2 = 8.
Cheat: Memorize 3 bits = 8 states.

A logical circuit can create a gate to compare inputs and generate an output.
The function of a two-input AND gate is that its output is high only when both inputs are high.
Hint: The word AND means both and all. All are high.

A chain of circuits called a shift register is used to make multiple decisions.
A shift register is a clocked array of circuits that passes data in steps along the way.

OSCILLATORS

The basic components of a sine wave oscillator are a filter and an amplifier operating in a feedback loop.

The frequency of an LC oscillator is determined by the inductance and capacitance in the tank circuit.
Hint: L stands for inductance and C for capacitance. An LC oscillator has both.

G7C – Transceiver design; filters; oscillators; digital signal processing (DSP)

TRANSMITTERS

To create single side band in a transmitter, first, a balanced modulator suppresses the unwanted carrier in an AM wave leaving two sidebands. Then, a filter removes the unwanted sideband resulting in a single sideband.
The output produced by a balanced modulator is double-sideband modulated RF.

Then, t**he circuit to select one of the sidebands from a balanced modulator is a filter.** *Hint: It filters out the unwanted sideband.*

A reason to use an impedance matching transformer at a transmitter output is to present the desired impedance to the transmitter and feed line.
Hint: Impedance matching matches the transmitter and feed line to transfer maximum power.

RECEIVERS

A product detector is used in a single sideband receiver to extract the modulated signal.
Hint: It detects and extracts the signal.

The parameter affecting receiver sensitivity is:
Input amplifier gain
Demodulator stage bandwidth
Input amplifier noise figure
All these choices are correct.
Hint: Gain, bandwidth and amplifier noise affect sensitivity.

SOFTWARE DEFINED RADIO

Software-defined radio (SDR) signal processing functions are performed by software. A software-defined radio (SDR) converts an incoming signal into two components. The I is "in-phase," and the Q is "quadrature," or 90 degrees out-of-phase.

The phase difference between the I and Q signals is 90 degrees.
Hint: Quad is four, and one-fourth of a circle is 90 degrees.

The advantage of using I and Q signals in SDRs is all types of modulation can be created with appropriate processing.
Hint: "Appropriate processing" can do anything.

The functions performed by software in a software-defined radio (SDR) are:
Filtering
Detection
Modulation
All of these choices are correct

FILTERS

Digital processing relies on software and is very flexible.
The advantage of a digital signal processing (DSP) filter compared to an analog filter is a wide range a filter bandwidths can be created.

A low-pass filter only passes frequencies below its design point.
The frequency above which a low-pass filter's output is less than half the input power is called the cutoff frequency.
Hint: A low-pass filter "cuts off" power above.

A band-pass filter passes above the bottom and below the top frequency.
The bandwidth of a band-pass filter is measured between the upper and lower half-power.
Hint: Bandwidth is between upper and lower.

The filter's maximum ability to reject signals outside its passband is called ultimate rejection.
Hint: Maximum rejection is ultimate.

The attenuation inside the passband is called insertion loss.
Hint: Even though the filter should pass everything inside the passband, there is always some loss inserting a filter.

DIRECT DIGITAL SYNTHESIZERS

An oscillator should be stable, so the frequency does not change. Digital synthesizers control frequency.

A characteristic of a Direct Digital Synthesizer is variable output frequency with the stability of a crystal oscillator.
Hint: Too complicated. Remember, "digital synthesizer is high-stability.

SUMMARY: PRACTICLE CIRCUITS

GROUP A – POWER SUPPLIES; SCHEMATIC SYMBOLS

Power supply filter uses capacitors and inductors. Bleeder resistor discharges filter capacitors.

Switchmode power supply's high frequency operation allows smaller components.

Portion of AC cycle converted to DC by a half-wave rectifier is 180 degrees.

Portion converted by a full-wave rectifier is 360 degrees.

Full-wave produces DC pulses at twice the frequency of the AC.

Two diodes and center-tapped transformer are full-wave.

Half-wave only requires one diode.

GROUP B – DIGITAL CIRCUITS; AMPLIFIERS; OSCILLATORS

Neutralize an amplifier to prevent self-oscillation.

A linear amplifier preserves input waveform

Efficiency of an amplifier is output power divided by input power.

Highest efficiency is Class C operation.

Class C is appropriate for FM.

Class A conducts 100% of the time.

A binary counter with 3 bits has 8 states.

AND gate output is high if both inputs are high.

Shift register is a clocked array in steps.

PRACTICAL CIRCUITS

Oscillator is a filter and amplifier in a feedback loop.

Frequency is determined by the inductance and capacitance.

GROUP C – DESIGN, FILTERS; OSCILLATORS; DSP

Receiver sensitivity is affected by input amplifier gain, demodulator bandwidth, and input amplifier noise filter.

A product detector extracts the modulated signals.

Output of a balanced modulator is double sideband.

To select one of the sidebands, use a filter.

Impedance matching transformer matches impedances.

Phase difference between I & Q is 90 degrees.

Advantage of I & Q signals in SDRs is all types of modulation can be created.

Functions performed in SDR are filtering, detection, and modulation.

DSP filter can create a wide range of bandwidths.

Low pass filter cutoff frequency is where output is half the input.

Bandpass filter bandwidth is measured between upper and lower half-power.

A filter's ability to reject is ultimate rejection.

Attenuation in a filter is insertion loss.

Direct Digital Synthesizer has stability of a crystal oscillator.

G8 – SIGNALS AND EMISSIONS

G8A – Carriers and modulation; AM; FM; single sideband; modulation envelope; digital modulation; overmodulation; link budgets and link margins

FSK is frequency-shift keying. The frequency shifts to produce different tones, which the receiver decodes. **Direct binary FSK is generated by changing the oscillator's frequency directly with a digital control signal.** *Hint: It is Direct binary, so you change frequency by changing the oscillator directly.*

Phase modulation is a method of frequency modulation. It sounds like FM, and you can decode phase modulation with FM circuits.
The process that changes the phase angle of an RF signal to convey information is phase modulation.
Hint: Modulation conveys information. "Changes the phase angle" = phase modulation.

The process that changes the instantaneous frequency of an RF wave to convey information is frequency modulation.
Hint: "Changes the frequency" = frequency modulation.

A reactance modulator creates phase modulation.
Hint: You react to phases.

In the AM Mode (amplitude modulation), modulation varies the amplitude of the radio wave.

The type of modulation that varies the instantaneous power level of the RF signal is amplitude modulation.
Hint: Power = amplitude.

QPSK modulation is a digital mode in which digital data is transmitted using 0, 90, 180, and 270 degrees phase shift to represent pairs of bits.
Hint: Too complicated! All you need to remember is QPSK uses phase shift.

QPSK31 is:
Sideband sensitive
Encoding provides error correction
Its bandwidth is about the same as BPSK31.
All these choices are correct

The narrowest phone emissions are on single sideband.

The modulation envelope of an AM signal is the waveform created by connecting the peak values of the modulated signal.
Cheat: Ditch the overly complicated question and answer. "Modulation envelope" in the question goes with "modulated signal" in the answer.

Overmodulation takes up excessive bandwidth.
Hint: You are overdoing it to excess.

Flat-topping is signal distortion caused by excessive drive. The excessive drive pushes the amplifier beyond its ability.

The FT8 digital mode uses 8-tone frequency shift keying modulation.
Hint: FT8 uses 8 tones.

A link budget is the sum of transmit power and antenna gains minus system losses as seen at the receiver.
Add up the gains and losses to calculate the net effect of the system. If you double your power (add 3 dB) then feed an antenna with 3 dB gain through coax with a 2 dB loss, the link budget is 3+3-2= 4 dB.

Link margin is the difference between the received power level and the minimum required signal level at the input of the receiver.
How much margin over the minimum required to hear.

G8B – Frequency changing; bandwidths of various modes; deviation; intermodulation

The mixer input varied to convert signals to an intermediate frequency is called a local oscillator.

Another term for the mixing of two RF signals is heterodyning.
Hint: that is why it is called a superheterodyne receiver.

Mixers mix everything and can create unwanted images.
The interference from a signal at twice the IF frequency from the desired signal is image response.
Hint: Ditch the overcomplicated question and math. Remember, the off-frequency interference is because of an image response.

The stage in a VHF FM transmitter that generates a harmonic of a lower frequency to reach the desired operating frequency is called a multiplier.
Hint: The harmonic is a multiple of the lower frequency.

SIGNALS AND EMISSIONS

When frequencies mix, the result is both the sum and the difference frequencies.
The combination of a mixer's Local Oscillator and RF input frequencies found in the output is the sum and difference.

INTERMODULATION

The process that combines two signals in a non-linear circuit or connection to produce unwanted spurious signals is called intermodulation.
Hint: You've probably heard intermod interference on your VHF radio. Intermodulation is unwanted.

The intermodulation products closest to the original signal frequencies are odd-order.
Confession: Explaining this odd question would take an entire book. Just memorize the odd answer.

An odd-order intermodulation product of frequencies F1 and F2 would be 2F1-F2.
Cheat: The only answer that adds up to an odd number (2+1+2).

BANDWIDTH

The amount of frequency jiggling on an FM signal is called deviation.
If the FM phone transmission has 5 kHz deviation and a 3 kHz modulating frequency, the total width is 16 kHz.
Solve: That is 5 + 3 = 8 on either side of the center for a total of 16.

The frequency deviation for a 12.21 MHz reactance modulated oscillator in a 5 kHz deviation, 146.520 MHz FM phone transmitter is 416.7 Hz.
Take this apart: The oscillator runs at 12.21 MHz and outputs 146.520 MHz, so the frequency is multiplied 12 times. The 12.21 MHz is where the deviation is applied, so the deviation is also multiplied 12 times.

Thus, the desired frequency deviation to get a 5 kHz result is 5/12 = 416.7 Hz.
Cheat: 416 Hz is an anagram for 146 MHz.

Receiver filtering provides selectivity and the ability to eliminate interference. Filters eliminate noise and interference outside the signal width.
It is good to match the receiver bandwidth to the bandwidth of the operating mode because it results in the best signal to noise ratio.

The relationship between transmitted symbol rate and bandwidth is **higher symbol rates require wider bandwidth.**
Hint: More information requires more space

DUTY CYCLES
Modes have different duty cycles, the ratio of time on to time off. CW is mostly off. SSB power varies with the audio. If you key the microphone and say nothing, there is no output. AM, FM and RTTY are 100% duty cycle. They transmit full power even if there is no audio. Long transmissions at a high duty cycle will cause the transmitter to overheat. Heat is the great enemy of solid-state components.
It is important to know the duty cycle of the mode you are transmitting as some modes have high duty cycles which could exceed the transmitter's average power rating.

G8C – Digital emission modes

Wi-Fi routers typically operate on 2.4 GHz.
Amateurs share channels with unlicensed Wi-Fi service on 2.4 GHz.

WSPR stands for Weak Signal Propagation Reporter.
WSPR is a digital mode used as a low-power beacon for assessing HF propagation.
Hint: Whisper is low power.

RTTY (teletype) uses a Baudot Code, invented by Emile Baudot in 1870.
Baudot is a 5-bit code with additional start and stop bits.
Hint: Remember Baudot is 5-bit.

The two separate frequencies used for FSK are called the Mark and Space. A computer or modem decodes the Mark and Space tones into letters.

Digital voice modes are DMR, D-STAR and SystemFusion.
Hint: You only need to recognize one of the three to see the right answer, "digital voice modes."

PACKET / PACTOR

Packet sends bursts of data called packets.
The header contains the routing and handling information.

With forward error correction, the transmission repeats itself, and the receiving station throws out whatever doesn't match.
Forward error correction (FEC) allows the receiver to correct errors in received packets by transmitting redundant information with the data.

A NAK response means the receiver is requesting the packet be retransmitted.
Hint: The word "NAK" sounds like a buzzer alarm – something is wrong – "send it again." Not AcKnowledged.

ARQ means Automatic Repeat reQuest.
The receiving station responds to an ARQ packet containing errors by requesting the packet be retransmitted.
Hint: If errors detected, retransmit.

The action that results from failure to exchange information due to excessive transmission attempts when using ARQ mode is, the connection is dropped.
If the message can't get through after repeated attempts, the system gives up.

PSK31and FT8

PSK31 is a weak signal digital mode using a warbling sound transmitted through the audio of the transmitter. The number of data bits in a single character varies with PSK.
Varicode is the type of code used for sending PSK31 characters.
Hint: The number of PSK data bits varies, and that is why it is "varicode."

Upper case letters use longer Varicode signals and thus slow down transmission.
Don't shout! Typing in all caps takes twice as long to send.

FT8 is a narrow-band digital mode that can receive signals with a very low signal-to-noise ratio.

FT8 signal reports refer to the signal-to-noise ratio.
An FT8 signal report of +3 indicates a signal-to-noise ratio equivalent to 3 dB in a 2.5 kHz bandwidth.
Hint: Remember it is signal-to-noise.

WATERFALL DISPLAY

On a waterfall display, frequency is horizontal; signal strength is intensity, and time is vertical.
Hint: Remember, "time is vertical." The display streams from top to bottom, with the bottom being the oldest.

Here is an example of PSK signals seen on a spectrum and waterfall display. The upper part shows the spectrum and the lower part, with vertical lines, are signals seen back in time, waterfall style. The waterfall streams from top to bottom, with the most recent part of the signal is at the top.

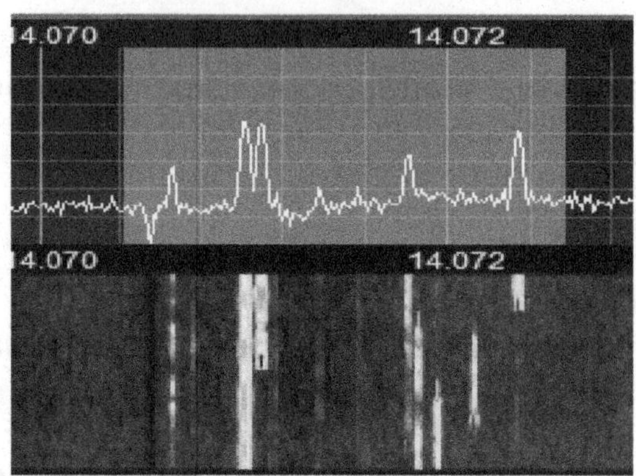

If you overdrive the transmitter in PSK mode (provide too much audio – "overmodulation"), the signal distorts. PSK is especially susceptible to overmodulation.
On a waterfall display, one or more vertical lines adjacent to a digital signal indicate overmodulation.
Hint: The vertical lines are overmodulation distortion. There don't appear to be any in this picture.

MESH NETWORK

In a mesh network, if one node fails, a packet may still reach its target station via an alternative route. The network is a mesh or spider web of interconnections. If a link breaks, the packet will eventually find its way through another route.

SUMMARY: SIGNALS AND EMISSIONS

GROUP A - Carriers and modulation, AM, FM, SSB, overmodulation, link budgets and margins

Generate FSK by changing oscillator frequency.

Change phase angle to convey phase modulation.

Change instantaneous frequency to general FM.

Reactance modulator creates phase modulation.

Change instantaneous power level to generate AM.

QPSK uses 0, 90, 180 and 270 degree phase shift.

QPSK31 is sideband sensitive, provides error correction, and has about same bandwidth as BPSK31.

Narrowest phone emissions are SSB.

AM modulation envelope is waveform that connects peak values.

Overmodulation takes up excessive bandwidth.

Flat-topping is distortion caused by excessive drive.

FT8 uses 8-tone frequency shift.

Link budget is sum of transmit power and antenna gains minus system losses.

Link margin is the difference between the received signal and the minimum needed at the input of the receiver.

GROUP B Frequency changing, bandwidths, deviation, intermodulation

Local oscillator converts signals to an intermediate frequency.

Mixing two RF signals is heterodyning.

Interference at twice the IF frequency is image response.

Stage that generates a harmonic to reach a frequency is a multiplier.

Combination of mixer's input frequencies is sum and difference.

Non-linear circuit produces intermodulation.

The closest to the original frequencies are odd-order.

Odd order would be 2F1-F2.

FM bandwidth is deviation plus modulating frequency times 2.

Frequency deviation for 12.21 MHz oscillator in a 5 kHz deviation, 156.52 transmitter is 416.7 Hz.

Match receiver bandwidth to mode for best signal to noise ratio.

Higher symbol rates require wider bandwidth.

Know the duty cycle so you don't exceed the transmitter's power rating.

GROUP C Digital emission modes

Amateurs share with unlicensed WIFI on 2.4 GHz.

WSPR is low-power beacon for assessing propagation.

Baudot is 5-bit code.

Two frequencies used for FSK are Mark and Space.

Digital voice modes are DMR, D-Star and SystemFusion.

A packet header contains routing and handling information.

Forward Error Correction transmits redundant information.

NAK response means "retransmit."

ARQ packet is requesting a retransmit.

ARQ disconnects if exchange fails after excessive attempts.

Varicode is used for PSK31.

Upper case letters slow down transmission.

FT8 is narrow band mode that can receive very low signal-to-noise ratio signals.

An FT8 signal report of +3 is a 3 dB signal-to-noise ratio.

A waterfall display shows frequency horizontal, signal strength is intensity and time is vertical.

One or more vertical lines on a waterfall indicate overmodulation.

In a mesh network, a packet may reach its destination via an alternate route.

PUT SOME FIRE IN YOUR WIRE – G9 – ANTENNAS AND FEED LINES

G9A – Feed lines; characteristic impedance and attenuation; SWR calculation; measurement and effects; antenna and feed point matching

CHARACTERISTIC IMPEDANCE AND ATTENUATION

The characteristic impedance of a parallel conductor antenna feed line is determined by the distance between the center conductors and the radius of the conductors.
Hint: The characteristic impedance of the line itself has nothing to do with length or frequency. By "characteristic," we mean, all by itself, with no outside influences. Dimensions determine the impedance.

The characteristic impedance of a dipole antenna is 50 ohms if close to the ground, or higher up 75 ohms. **The typical characteristic impedance of coaxial cables used in amateur stations is 50 and 75 ohms.**

Window line is a flat cable with two wires separated by strips of insulating plastic. Gaps in the insulation look like windows, hence the name. Window line has extremely low losses, 1/10 the loss in coaxial cable. **The nominal impedance of "window line" parallel transmission line is 450 ohms.**

"Attenuation" describes a loss of signal.
The attenuation of coaxial cable increases as the frequency increases.
Hint: Higher frequency = higher losses. Operating frequency often determines your choice of coax.

Coax specifications include power handling ability, impedance, attenuation, and resistance to sunlight.
RF feed line loss is expressed in terms of Decibels per 100 feet.
Feed line loss has two components. The line itself has loss, and there is additional loss in the line because of high SWR. Both increase with frequency.

SWR

Power reflected back from the antenna is evidence of a mismatch. Standing Wave Ratio or SWR is a measure of the mismatch.
A higher SWR represents a larger mismatch and increases loss in a lossy transmission line.
Higher SWR equals higher losses. Measure SWR by comparing the output power to the power reflected down the line.

Reflected power at the point where a feed line connects to an antenna is caused by a difference between the feed line impedance and the antenna feed point impedance.
Hint: A mismatch causes reflected power.

To prevent standing waves on the antenna feed line, the antenna feed point impedance must be matched to the characteristic impedance of the feed line.
Hint: Matching the impedances transfers maximum power and minimizes reflected power.

You can calculate the SWR by comparing the impedance of the line to the impedance of the antenna. The questions are simple examples:

Connect a 50-ohm feed line to a 200-ohm load and the SWR is 200/50 = 4:1

Connect a 50-ohm feed line to a 10-ohm load and the SWR is 50/10 = 5:1

Hint: Notice the higher number always goes on top, so your ratio turns out to be x:1

Attenuation or "line loss" also increases with higher SWR.
If a transmission line is lossy, high SWR will increase the loss.
Hint: Higher SWR = higher losses.

Line loss can mask the measurement of high SWR because the reflected power is attenuated (lost) in the line. Some of the reflected power never reaches the meter and results in a lower reading.
Higher line loss reduces SWR measured at the input to the line.

If the SWR is too high to match the transmitter, we can insert an antenna tuner to bring down the SWR at the transmitter end. However, this does not change the mismatch where the feed line meets the antenna.
If the SWR on the antenna feed line is 5:1, and you use a matching network at the transmitter to adjust it down to 1:1, the SWR on the feed line is still 5:1.
Hint: The SWR on the feed line does not change, only that seen by the transmitter.

G9B – Basic Dipole and monopole antennas

I told the salesman I needed some antenna wire. He asked me, "How long?" I thought that was an odd question, so I answered, "I'm building an antenna. I guess I'll need it for a long time." He coax-ed me out the door.

How long should an antenna be? The classic and most fundamental antenna is a half-wavelength long wire, split in the middle, and fed with coax. If you think about the current flowing in the wire, it will start high in the middle at the feed point, and by the time it gets to the end, the cycle reverses. Nothing is left over, and nothing reflects back.

What if you took a single piece of wire and fed it at the end?
The characteristic of a random wire HF antenna connected directly to the transmitter is station equipment may carry significant RF current.
You need to have a good ground connection to act as the "other half" of the antenna, or you are it!

A quarter-wave is half of a half-wave, and the impedance is also half the characteristic impedance of the half-wave antenna. A half-wave antenna in free space has an impedance of 72 ohms. So, the characteristic impedance of a quarter-wave antenna in free space is about 36 ohms.

If the vertical antenna is above the ground, you can raise the impedance by making it look more like a dipole.
To adjust the feed point impedance to be approximately 50 ohms, slope the radials downward.
Hint: Make it look more like a vertical dipole.

"Azimuth" or "azimuthal" refers to compass direction.
A quarter-wave ground-plane vertical antenna is omnidirectional in azimuth.
Hint: A vertical antenna radiates equally poorly in all directions.

Dipoles radiate off their sides.
The radiation pattern of a dipole antenna in free space is a figure-eight at right angles to the antenna.

The pattern changes as the antenna gets lower because of reflection off the ground. Ground reflection fills in the gaps.

ANTENNAS AND FEED LINES

If a horizontal antenna is less than a half wavelength high, the azimuthal pattern is almost omnidirectional.

Radials are wires coming out the bottom or ground side of a quarter-wave vertical antenna. They act as the other half of a dipole and connect to the coax shield.
On a ground-mounted vertical antenna, the radials are placed on the surface of the Earth or buried a few inches below the ground.
Hint: The antenna is ground-mounted. Where else could the radials go?

Radials help form the other half of the antenna, but the proximity to ground means the ground absorbs some of the energy.
An advantage of a horizontally polarized antenna as compared to a vertically polarized HF antenna is lower ground reflection losses.

Height above ground also influences the impedance of an antenna.
The impedance of a half-wave dipole steadily decreases as it is reduced to 1/10 wavelength above ground.
Hint: Lower antenna = lower impedance.

If we move the feed point of the antenna from the center to the ends, the feed point impedance steadily increases.
Hint: Off center = higher impedance.

ANTENNA LENGTHS

A half-wavelength antenna is half a wavelength long. The formula to use is 468 / frequency = feet. That 468 is a handy number. You will use it often in your ham career. Figure using 468, and cut the antenna a little longer. Then, trim it down to minimize the SWR. It is easier to shorten than to add wire.

A one-half wave dipole antenna cut for 14.250 MHz would be 468/14.250 = 32.8 feet. The closest answer on the test is 33 feet.

A half-wave dipole antenna cut for 3.550 MHz would be 468/3.550 = 131.83 feet. The closest test answer is 132 feet.
Hint: Don't be thrown off by the fact your calculator gives you a slightly different answer. Pick the closest.

Many verticals are half a dipole - quarter-wave on one side, and the ground, radials, or the vehicle body provides the other half of the antenna. If you know the frequency, the magic number is 234 (half of 468). Divide 234 by the frequency, and you get the length of a quarter-wave in feet.
A quarter wave vertical cut for 28.5 MHz would be 234/28.5 = 8.21 feet. The closest answer is 8 feet.

G9C – Directional antennas

Yagis, Quads, and Dishes are all directional antennas. They concentrate the signal in one direction and reject signals to the back and side of the antenna.

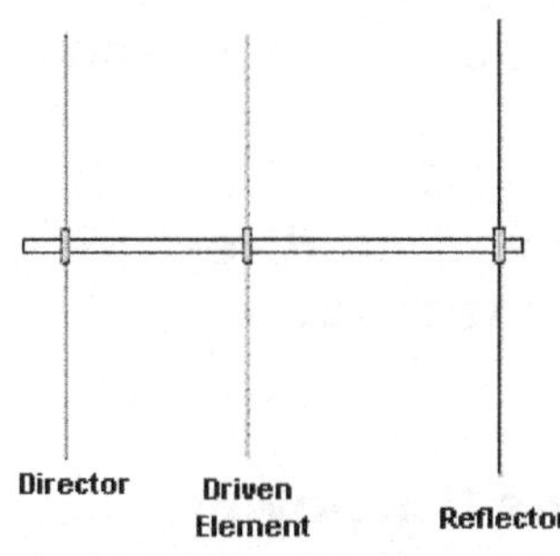

This is an example of a Yagi antenna. The drawing shows it in a vertical orientation. Usually, it would be horizontal so imagine you are looking down at it from above.

A three-element Yagi consists of a director, a driven element, and a reflector.
The reflector is longer, and the director is shorter than the driven element.

ANTENNAS AND FEED LINES

The driven element is where power is applied. It is a dipole.
The approximate length of the driven element is one-half wavelength.

To increase the bandwidth of a Yagi antenna, use larger diameter elements.
"Bandwidth" describes the range of frequencies the antenna can operate with a reasonable SWR. *Hint: Increase the width to increase the bandwidth.*

The gain of an antenna is the increase in signal strength in a specific direction compared to a reference antenna. dBi gain means compared to an isotropic antenna, and dBd gain is compared to a dipole antenna. An isotropic antenna assumes a point source that radiates equally in all directions in space. A dipole concentrates energy at its sides and is stronger in its strongest direction than an isotropic source by about 2.15 dB.

When antenna gain is stated in dBi, the gain figures will seem 2.15 dB higher than the same antenna gain stated in dBd.
If an antenna maker wants to inflate his advertising, he will compare his antenna to the weaker isotropic source. Using dBi comparisons makes the antenna look like it has more gain.

Increasing boom length and adding directors increases the gain of a Yagi antenna.
Hint: Increasing is gain.

The front-to-back ratio means the power radiated in the major direction lobe as compared to the power radiated in exactly the opposite direction.
Hint: Power to the front vs. power to the back.

The "main lobe" of a directive antenna is the direction of maximum radiated field.

You can also increase the gain by stacking antennas. **The gain from two three-element Yagis spaced vertically would be approximately 3 dB.**
Hint: Two antennas, twice the gain. Remember, 3 dB is double.

Yagi antenna design variables that can be adjusted to optimize forward gain, front-to-back ratio and SWR bandwidth are:
Physical length of the boom
Number of elements on the boom
Spacing of each element along the boom.
All these choices are correct.
Hint: Yagi design is a trade-off of these three variables.

Interaction among the elements of a Yagi antenna lowers the feed point impedance. A gamma match matches the relatively low feed point impedance to 50 ohms by moving the feed point off center.
An advantage of the gamma match is it does not require the driven element to be insulated from the boom.
That makes the antenna easier to build.

There are other matching methods.
A beta or hairpin match is a shorted transmission line placed at the feed point of a Yagi antenna to provide impedance matching.
Cheat: A hairpin is short.

G9D – Specialized antenna types and applications

Suppose you wanted an antenna that would be good for statewide communication. That would require a high radiation angle to bounce off the ionosphere and come back down within a few hundred kilometers.
The most effective antenna for NVIS short -skip communication on 40 meters during the day would be a horizontal dipole placed between 1/10 and 1/4 wavelength above ground.
NVIS means Near Vertical Incidence Skywave. The NVIS antenna is low to the ground and works because the signal reflects off the nearby ground and goes up at a high angle.
Hint: Look for the answer that is closest to the ground, 1/10 wavelength.

End-fed antennas are handy for field operations. They only require one support.
The feed point impedance of an end-fed half-wave antenna is very high.
Use a matching transformer to bring the impedance down.

Another single-support antenna is the inverted V.
The common name of a dipole with a single central support is an inverted v.
Hint: It looks like an upside-down V.

A "halo" antenna is a horizontal loop.
The maximum radiation from a portable VHF/UHF "halo" antenna is omnidirectional in the plane of the halo.

A small loop (less than 1/10 wavelength in circumference) has nulls in its radiation pattern broadside to the loop.
Use those nulls for direction finding.

Antenna traps are tuned circuits that adjust the electrical length of the antenna.
The primary purpose of antenna traps is to permit multiband operation.
Here's an over-simplified illustration: The element would be half-wave for 20 meters (about 33 feet or 16.5 feet on a side). The 15-meter trap would be inserted at 11 feet. A 20-meter signal will pass through the trap and use the full-size element. A 15-meter signal will be trapped or isolated from the end. The shorter portion resonates on 15 meters.

The disadvantage of multiband antennas is that they have poor harmonic rejection.
The antenna works on multiple bands. A tri-band (20/15/10 Meter) Yagi will radiate the second harmonic of the 20-meter signal on 10 meters.

A log periodic is another type of directional antenna.
It is called a log periodic because the length and spacing of the elements increase logarithmically along the boom.

The advantage of a log periodic is its wide bandwidth. Log periodic antennas can cover many bands on one antenna boom without using tuned circuits called "traps."

"Screwdriver" antennas are popular for mobile operation. A physically short antenna uses an inductor (coil) to make it electrically longer. An electric motor tunes the antenna by varying the tap point of the inductor and, therefore, its length.
A screwdriver antenna adjusts its feed-point impedance by varying the base loading inductance.

A Beverage antenna system is used for directional receiving on MF and low HF bands.

The Beverage is a long wire close to the ground to minimize the noise received on lower HF bands.

The advantage of vertically stacking horizontally polarized Yagi antennas is it narrows the main lobe elevation.
Hint: Stacking antennas concentrates the signal.

SUMMARY: ANTENNAS AND FEEDLINES

GROUP A FEED LINES; SWR; FEED POINT MATCHING

Impedance of parallel feed line is determined by line separation and radius of conductors.

Characteristic impedance of amateur coax is 50 and 75 ohms.

Window line is 450 ohms.

Attenuation increases as frequency increases.

RF feed line loss is expressed in decibels per 100 feet.

Higher SWR means higher mismatch and losses.

Reflected power is caused by difference in feed line and antenna impedance.

To prevent standing waves, match impedances.

Calculate SWR by finding the ratio of impedances.

Lossy transmission line shows higher losses with high SWR.

Higher line loss reduces SWR measured at the input.
An antenna tuner matches the transmitter but the SWR on the line does not change.

GROUP B BASIC DIPOLE AND MONOPOLE

Random wire antenna may cause significant current on equipment.

Slope vertical radials downward to make the impedance 50 ohms.

Ground-plane vertical is omnidirectional.

Dipole pattern is figure 8 at right angles to wire.

Low horizontal antenna is omnidirectional.

Ground mounted vertical has radials on or in ground.

Horizontal antenna has less ground loss than vertical.

Impedance of dipole decreases as reduced to 1/10 wavelength above ground.

Feed point toward the end increases impedance.

Half-wave dipole is 468 divided by frequency in MHz.

Quarter wave is 234 divided by frequency in MHz.

GROUP C DIRECTIONAL ANTENNAS

Reflector is longer, director is shorter than driven element on directional antenna.

Driven element is one-half wavelength.

Increase bandwidth with larger diameter elements.

Antenna gain in dBi will seem 2.15 dB higher than gain in dBd.

Increasing boom length and adding directors increases gain.

Front-to-back ratio compares power in major direction vs that in the opposite direction.

Main lobe is maximum radiated field.

Gain of two stacked Yagis is 3 dB.

Optimize antenna by adjusting length of boom, number of elements, and element spacing.

Gamma match does not require driven element to be insulated from boom.

Beta or hairpin match provide impedance matching.

GROUP D SPECIALIZED ANTENNA TYPES

NVIS is dipole 1/10 to 1/4 wavelength above ground.

End-fed antenna impedance is very high.

Dipole with one support is inverted V.

Halo antenna is omnidirectional.

Small loop has nulls broadside.

Antenna traps permit multiband operation.

Multiband antennas have poor harmonic rejection.

ANTENNAS AND FEED LINES

Log periodic antenna varies spacing and length logarithmically.

Log periodic has wide bandwidth.

Screwdriver antenna varies base loading inductance

Stacking Yagi antennas lowers the main lobe elevation.

Beverage antenna is used for directional receiving.

G0 – ELECTRICAL AND RF SAFETY

G0A – RF safety principles; rules and guidelines; routine station evaluation

A microwave oven heats with radio waves.
RF energy can heat human body tissue.

To determine RF exposure use the following:
Duty cycle
Frequency
Power density.
All these choices are correct.
Hint: All affect the amount of heating.

How can you determine if your station complies with FCC RF exposure regulations?
Calculation based on FCC OET Bulletin 65
Calculation based on computer modeling
Measurement of field strength.
All these choices are correct.
Hint: Calculation and measurements.

"Time-averaging," in reference to RF exposure, is the total RF exposure averaged over a certain period.
Hint: Time averaging is averaging over a time period.

If an evaluation shows you exceed the permissible limits, you must take action to prevent human exposure to the excessive RF fields.
Hint: If you exceed the permissible limits, take action!

The stations subject to FCC rules on RF exposure are all stations with a time-averaged transmission of more than one milliwatt.
Hint: "One milliwatt" is just about everybody.

SAFETY

If your station fails to meet the FCC RF exposure exemption criteria, you must perform an RF exposure evaluation in accordance with FCC OET Bulletin 65.
Hint: Don't worry about the Bulletin number. Just know if you are over one milliwatt, you must do an evaluation.

The effect of modulation duty cycle on RF exposure is a lower transmitter duty cycle permits greater short-term exposure.
Hint: Your body has time to cool down when the transmitter is silent.

To ensure compliance with RF safety regulations, perform a routine RF exposure evaluation and prevent access to any identified high exposure areas.
Hint: To ensure compliance, evaluate.

To accurately measure RF field strength, use a calibrated field strength meter with a calibrated antenna.
Hint: It makes sense to measure field strength with a field strength meter.

If evaluation shows the neighbor may receive more than the allowable limit of RF exposure from the main lobe of a directional antenna, take precautions to ensure the antenna cannot be pointed in that direction when they are present.
Hint: Too many words! Point your directional antenna away from the neighbor.

If you install an antenna indoors, make sure the MPE limits are not exceeded in occupied areas.
"MPE" is maximum permissible exposure.
Hint: You always want to make sure you don't exceed the MPE limits, indoors or out.

G0B- Station safety; electrical shock; safety grounding; fusing; interlocks; wiring; antenna and tower safety

In a four-conductor connection operating from a 240 VAC circuit, the wires to attach to the fuses or circuit breakers are only the hot wires.
Hint: Hot wires carry the power. The fuses or circuit breakers trip with excess amperage. Grounds aren't connected to the breakers.

A ground fault circuit interrupter (GFCI) will disconnect AC power if it detects current flowing from one or more of the hot wires directly to ground.
When electricity flows from hot to ground, it is usually through a person. A GFCI protects against electrical shock by disconnecting.

Smaller AWG (American Wire Gauge) numbers mean larger wire size. AWG 4 is quite stout, while AWG 26 is like a thread.
The minimum wire size for a circuit that draws 20 amperes is AWG 12.

A circuit that uses AWG 14 wire would take a 15-ampere circuit breaker.
Hint: Smaller wire, smaller circuit breaker.

The National Electrical Code covers electrical safety of the station.

The goal of lightning protection is to keep the charge outside your house.
A station's lightning protection ground system should be outside the building.

Lightning arrestors should be located where the feed lines enter the building.
Hint: Keep it outside.

SAFETY

Lightning protection grounds must be bonded together with all other grounds.
Even a few ohms difference between two "grounds" can cause a tremendous amount of current to flow in response to a high-voltage lightning strike. Like a boat riding a wave, you want all the equipment to rise and fall together.

When climbing a tower with a safety belt or harness, confirm the belt is rated for the weight of the climber and is within its allowable service life.
Hint: This question is tricky because all the answers look good. Remember, to save a life—stay in the service life.

Before climbing a tower that supports electrically powered devices, make sure all circuits that supply power are locked out and tagged.
Locked out means turned off.

A danger from lead-tin solder is that lead can contaminate food if you don't wash your hands.
Hint: Mom told you to wash your hands.

Solder joints are not used to connect the base of a tower to ground because a solder joint will likely be destroyed by the heat of a lightning strike.
Solder is conductive but melts.
Hint: Heat melts solder.

SUMMARY: ELECTRICAL AND RF SAFETY

GROUP A RF SAFETY; STATION EVALUATION

RF energy can heat human tissue.

RF exposure depends on duty cycle, frequency, and power density.

Determine compliance with calculations based on FCC Bulletin, computer modeling, and measurements.

Time-averaging is RF exposure averaged over time.

If evaluation shows exceeding limits, take action.

Subject to RF exposure rules if more than one milliwatt. If so, must perform exposure evaluation.

To ensure compliance, prevent access to high exposure areas.

Lower duty cycle permits longer short-term exposure.

If evaluation shows neighbors may be overexposed, ensure the antenna can't be pointed toward them.

Don't exceed MPE limits with an indoor antenna.

GROUP B STATION SAFETY, ELECTRIC SHOCK; GROUNDING; FUSING; ANTENNA AND TOWER SAFETY

Only hot wires are attached to fuses.

20-amp circuit needs AWG 12 wire.

15-amp circuit needs AWG 14 wire.

National Electrical Code covers electrical safety in the station.

Lightning protection should be outside the building.

Lightning arrestors should be where the feed lines enter the building.

Bond lightning protection grounds with all grounds.

Tower climbing belt should be rated and within allowable service life.

Make sure all circuits are locked out and tagged.

Lead-tin solder can contaminate food. Wash up.

Lightning will destroy solder joints.

Congratulations! You're done, Be sure to check out the bonus chapter at the end, "Learning CW," Hope to hear you on the air soon. 73/DX k4ia

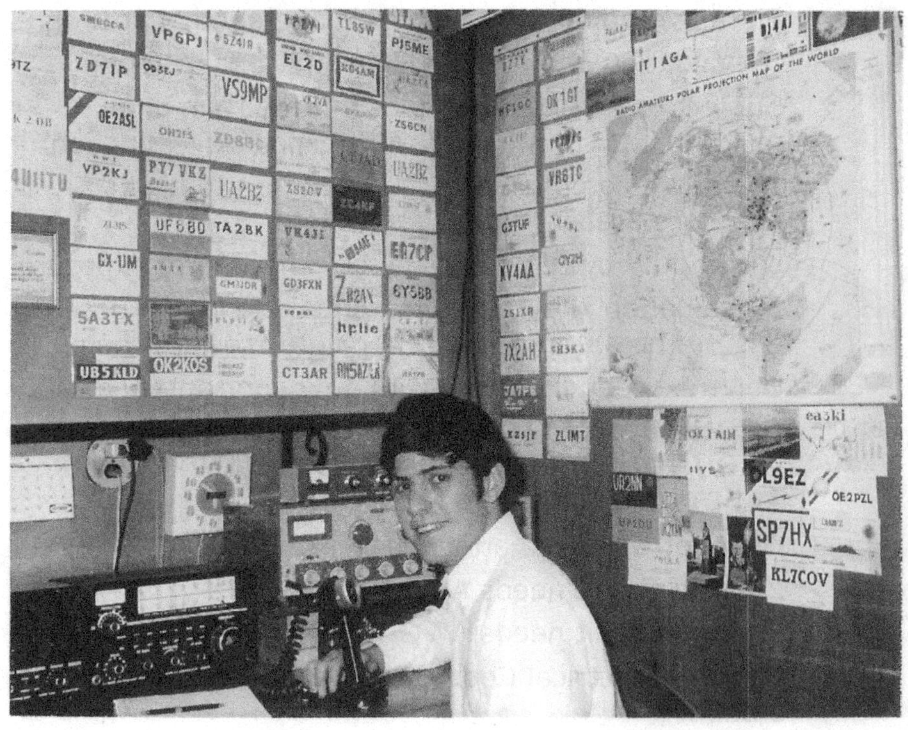

K4IA as WA4TUF in 1967

REVIEW AMATEUR RADIO GENERAL CLASS QUESTIONS & ANSWERS

The question pool is Sub-elements and Groups within Sub-elements. You get one question from each of the 35 Groups, 35 questions.

SUBELEMENT G1 - COMMISSION'S RULES

[5 Exam Questions - 5 Groups]

G1A - General Class control operator frequency privileges; primary and secondary allocations

G1A01 A General Class license may not transmit on portions of the
80, 40, 20 and 15 meter bands.

G1A02 Phone operation is prohibited on
30 meters.

G1A03 Image transmission is prohibited on
30 meters.

G1A04 The amateur band restricted to communication on only specific channels, rather than frequency ranges is
60 meters.

G1A05 A frequency where a General Class operator may not be the control operator is
7.125 to 7.175 MHz

G1A06 When the FCC rules designate the amateur service as a secondary user,
amateur users must not cause harmful interference to primary users and must accept interference from primary users.

G1A07 Within the 10-meter band, a General Class operator may transmit CW
in the entire band.

G1A08 Bands with segments allocated exclusively to Amateur Extra Class licensees are
80 meters, 40 meters, 20 meters, and 15 meters.

G1A09 A frequency within the General Class portion of the 15-meter band is
21300 kHz.

G1A10 The portion of the 10-meter band available for repeater use is
the portion above 29.5 MHz.

G1A11 When General Class licensees are not permitted to use the entire voice portion of a particular band, the portion of the voice segment generally available to General Class licensees is
the upper-frequency portion.

G1B - Antenna structure limitations; good engineering and good amateur practice; beacon operation; prohibited transmissions; retransmitting radio signals

G1B01 The maximum height above ground to which an antenna structure may be erected without requiring notification to the FAA and registration with the FCC provided it is not at or near a public-use airport, is
200 feet.

G1B02 A condition for beacon stations is,
there must be no more than one beacon signal transmitting in the same band from the same station location.

G1B03 The purpose of a beacon station is
observation of propagation and reception.

G1B04 **Occasional retransmission of weather and propagation forecast information from US government stations** is permitted.

G1B05 One-way transmissions are permitted
necessary to assist in learning Morse code.

G1B06 State and local governments are permitted to regulate amateur radio antenna structures, but
Amateur Service communications must be reasonably

accommodated, and regulations must constitute the minimum practical to accommodate the legitimate purpose of the state or local entity.

G1B07 Abbreviations or procedural signals in the Amateur Service may be used
if they do not obscure the meaning of a message.

G1B08 It is permissible to communicate with amateur stations in countries outside the areas administered by the Federal Communication Commission when the contact is with amateurs in any country
except those who have notified the ITU that they object to such communication.

G1B09 Automatically controlled beacons are permitted between
28.2 and 28.3 MHz.

G1B10 The power limit for beacon stations is
100 watts.

G1B11 Good engineering and good amateur practice as applied to the operation of an amateur station in all aspects not covered by the Part 97 rules are determined by the
FCC.

G1C - Transmitter power regulations; data emission standard; 60-meter operation requirements

G1C01 The maximum transmitting power an amateur station may use on 10.140 MHz is
200 watts PEP output.

G1C02 The maximum transmitting power an amateur station may use on the 12-meter band is
1500 watts PEP output.

G1C03 The maximum bandwidth permitted by FCC rules for amateur radio stations transmitting on USB frequencies in the

REVIEW – COMMISSION'S RULES

60-meter band is
2.8 kHz.

G1C04 On the 60-meter band, if you are using an antenna other than a dipole,
you must keep a record of the gain of the antenna.

G1C05 The limitation on transmitter power on the 28 MHz band for a General Class control operator is
1,500 watts PEP output.

G1C06 The limitation on transmitter power on the 1.8 MHz band is
1500 watts PEP output

G1C07 Before using a new digital protocol on the air,
publicly document the technical characteristics of the protocol.

G1C08 The maximum symbol rate permitted for RTTY or data emission transmitted at frequencies below 28 MHz is
300 baud.

GC1C09 The maximum power limit on the 60-meter band is
ERP of 100 watts with respect to a dipole.

G1C10 The maximum symbol rate permitted for RTTY or data emission transmissions on the 10-meter band is
1200 baud.

G1C11 The measurement specified by the FCC rules that regulate maximum power is
PEP output from the transmitter.

G1D - Volunteer Examiners and Volunteer Examiner Coordinators; temporary identification; element credit; remote operation

G1D01 An expired amateur radio license may be used for credit for the elements represented by
any person who can demonstrate that they once held an FCC-issued General, Advanced, or Amateur Extra class license that was not revoked by the FCC.

G1D02 If you are an accredited VE holding a General Class operator license, you may administer a licensing exam to a
Technician only.

G1D03 If you are a Technician Class operator and have a CSCE for General Class privileges, you may operate
on any General or Technician Class band segment.

G1D04 To administer a Technician Class license examination,
at least three General Class or higher VEs must observe the examination.

G1D05 When operating a US station by remote control from outside the country, the control operator must have
a US operator/primary station license.

G1D06 Until an upgrade is shown in the FCC database, a Technician must identify with "AG" after their call
whenever they operate using General Class privileges.

G1D07 Volunteer Examiners are accredited by
a Volunteer Examiner Coordinator.

G1D08 For a non-US citizen to be an accredited Volunteer Examiner,
the person must hold an FCC-granted amateur radio license of General Class or above.

REVIEW - COMMISSION'S RULES

G1D09 A Certificate of Successful Completion of Examination (CSCE) is valid for exam element credit for **365 days.**

G1D10 The minimum age that one must be to qualify as an accredited Volunteer Examiner is
18 years.

G1D11 If a person has an expired FCC-issued amateur radio license of General Class or higher, and the two-year grace period has expired, to recover the license
the applicant must show proof of the expired license and pass the current element 2 exam (Technician).

G1D12 When operating a station in South America by remote control over the Internet from the US,
only the regulations of the remote station's country apply. The place of the transmitter determines the rules. Remote control is a long microphone cord.

G1E – Control categories; repeater regulations; third party rules; ITU regions; automatically controlled digital station

G1E01 A third party would be disqualified from participating in stating a message over an amateur station if
the third party's amateur license has been revoked and not reinstated.

G1E02 A 10-meter repeater may retransmit the 2-meter signal from a station having a Technician Class control operator
only if the 10-meter repeater control operator holds at least a General Class license.

G1E03 To conduct communications with a digital station operating under automatic control outside the automatic control band segments,
the station initiating the contact must be under local or remote control.

G1E04 A licensed amateur radio operator must take specific steps to avoid harmful interference to other users or facilities when:
Operating within one mile of an FCC Monitoring Station.
Using a band where the Amateur Service is secondary.
A station is transmitting spread spectrum emissions.
All these choices are correct.

G1E05 The types of messages for a third party in another country that an amateur station may transmit are
only messages relating to amateur radio or of a personal character or relating to emergencies or disaster relief.

G1E06 The frequency allocations applying to amateurs in North and South America are for
ITU Region 2.

G1E07 The part of the 2.4 GHz band where amateurs may communicate with non-licensed Wi-Fi stations is
no part.

G1E08 The maximum PEP output allowed for spread spectrum transmissions is
10 watts.

G1E09 Messages sent via digital modes are exempt from Part 97 third-party rules
never.

G1E10 An amateur should avoid transmitting on 14.100, 18.110, 21.150, 24.930, and 28.200 because
a system of propagation beacon stations operates on those frequencies.

G1E11 Automatically controlled stations transmitting RTTY or data emissions may communicate with other automatically controlled digital stations

anywhere in the 6-meter or shorter wavelength bands, and in limited segments of some HF bands.

G1E12 Third party messages may be transmitted via remote control
under any circumstances under which third party messages are permitted by FCC rules.

SUBELEMENT G2 - OPERATING PROCEDURES

[5 Exam Questions - 5 Groups]

G2A - Phone operating procedures; USB/LSB conventions; breaking into a contact; transmitter setup for voice operation: answering DX stations

G2A01 The sideband most commonly used for voice communications on frequencies of 14 MHz or higher is
upper sideband.

G2A02 The mode most commonly used for voice communications on the 160-meter, 75-meter, and 40-meter bands is
lower sideband.

G2A03 The commonly used mode for SSB voice communications in the VHF and UHF bands is
upper sideband.

G2A04 The mode most commonly used for voice communications on the 17-meter and 12-meter bands is
upper sideband.

G2A05 The mode of voice communication most commonly used on the HF amateur bands is
single sideband.

G2A06 An advantage when using single sideband compared to other analog voice modes on the HF amateur bands is
less bandwidth used and greater power efficiency.

G2A07 In single sideband voice mode,
only one sideband is transmitted; the other sideband and carrier are suppressed.

G2A08 A recommended way to break into a contact when using phone is to
say your call sign once.

G2A09 Most amateur stations use lower sideband on the 160-meter, 75-meter, and 40-meter bands because it is
commonly accepted amateur practice.

REVIEW – OPERATING PROCEDURES

G2A10 A difference between voice VOX operation versus PTT operation is
VOX allows "hands-free" operation.

G2A11 When a station in the contiguous 48 states calls "CQ DX," you would respond if you were
outside the lower 48 states.

G2A12 The control adjusted for proper ALC setting on a single sideband transceiver is the
transmit audio or microphone gain.

G2B - Operating effectively; band plans; drills and emergencies, RACES operation

G2B01 **Except during emergencies, no amateur station has priority access to any frequency.**

G2B02 The first thing you should do if you are communicating with another amateur station and hear a station in distress break in is
acknowledge the station in distress and determine what assistance may be needed.

G2B03 If propagation changes during your contact and you notice increasing interference from other activity on the same frequency,
attempt to resolve the interference problem in a mutually acceptable manner.

G2B04 When selecting a CW transmitting frequency, the minimum separation that should be used to minimize interference to stations on adjacent frequencies is
150 to 500 Hz.

G2B05 When selecting an SSB transmitting frequency, the minimum frequency separation is
2 kHz to 3 kHz.

G2B06 A practical way to avoid harmful interference on an apparently clear frequency before calling CQ on CW or phone is to
send "QRL?" on CW, followed by your call sign; or, if

using phone, ask if the frequency is in use, followed by your call sign.

G2B07 When choosing a frequency on which to initiate a call, good amateur practice is to
follow the voluntary band plan.

G2B08 The voluntary band plan for transmitting within the 48 contiguous states in the 50.1 to 50.125 MHz segment is for **contacts not within the 48 contiguous states**.

G2B09 The control operator of an amateur station transmitting in RACES to assist relief operations during a disaster must be
only a person holding an FCC-issued amateur operator license.

G2B10 Good practice for net management is to
have a backup frequency in case of interference or poor conditions.

G2B11 RACES drill may be routinely conducted without special authorization
no more than 1 hour per week.

G2C - CW operating and procedures and procedural signals; Q signals; full break-in

G2C01 Full break-in telegraphy (QSK) is described as
transmitting stations can receive between code characters and elements.

G2C02 If a CW station sends "QRS,"
send slower.

G2C03 When a CW operator sends "KN" at the end of a transmission, it means
listening only for a specific station or stations.

G2C04 The Q signal "QRL?" means
"Are you busy?" or "Is this frequency in use?"

G2C05 The best speed to use when answering a CQ in Morse code is

the fastest speed you are comfortable copying but no faster than the CQ.

G2C06 The term "zero beat" in CW operation means
matching your transmit frequency to the frequency of a received signal.

G2C07 When sending CW, a "C" added to the RST report means a
chirpy or unstable signal.

G2C08 The prosign sent to indicate the end of a formal message when using CW is
AR.

G2C09 The Q signal "QSL" means
I have received and understood.

G2C10 The Q signal "QRN" means
I am troubled by static.

G2C11 The Q signal "QRV" means
I am ready to receive messages.

G2D – Volunteer Monitoring Program; HF operations

G2D01 The Volunteer Monitoring Program is
Amateur volunteers who are formally enlisted to monitor the airwaves for rules violations.

G2D02 Objectives of the Volunteer Monitoring Program are
to encourage amateur radio operators to self-regulate and comply with the rules.

G2D03 Volunteer Monitors may localize a station whose continuous carrier is holding a repeater by
comparing beam headings on the repeater input from their home locations.

G2D04 An azimuthal projection map is a
map that shows true bearings and distances from a particular location.

G2D05 If you are looking for a contact with any station,
repeat "CQ" a few times, followed by "this is," and then

your call sign a few times, then pause to listen, repeat as necessary.

G2D06 When making a "long-path" contact with another station, a directional antenna is pointed
180 degrees from its short-path heading.

G2D07 The NATO Phonetic Alphabet uses
Alpha, Bravo, Charlie, Delta.

G2D08 Many amateurs keep a station log
to help with a reply if the FCC requests information.

G2D09 When participating in a contest on HF frequencies,
identify your station per normal FCC regulations.

G2D10 QRP operation is **l**
ow power transmit operation.

G2D11 Signal reports are typically exchanged at the beginning of an HF contact
to allow each station to operate according to conditions.

G2E - Digital mode operating procedures

G2E01 The mode normally used when sending an RTTY signal via AFSK with an SSB transmitter is
LSB.

G2E02 VARA is
a digital protocol used with Winlink.

G2E03 The symptoms that may result from other signals interfering with a PACTOR or VARA transmission are:
Frequent retries or timeouts.
Long pauses in message transmission.
Failure to establish a connection between stations.
All these choices are correct.

G2E04 When choosing a transmit frequency to answer a station calling CQ using FT8,
find a clear frequency during the alternate time slot to the calling station.

REVIEW - OPERATING PROCEDURES

G2E05 The standard sideband used to generate a JT65, JT9 or FT8 digital signal when using AFSK in any amateur band is **USB.**

G2E06 The most common frequency shift for RTTY emissions in the amateur HF bands is
170 Hz.

G2E07 When using FT8, you need
computer time accurate within 1 second.

G2E08 The segment of the 20-meter band where most digital operations are commonly found is
between 14.070 MHz and 14.100 MHz.

G2E09 To join a contact between two stations using the PACTOR protocol,
joining an existing contact is not possible, PACTOR connections are limited to two stations.

G2E10 The way to establish contact with a digital messaging system gateway station is to
transmit a connect message on the station's published frequency.

G2E11 The primary purpose of an Amateur Radio Emergency Data Network (AREDN) is **to provide high-speed data services during an emergency or community event.**

G2E12 Winlink is:
An amateur radio wireless network to send and receive email on the Internet
A form of Packet Radio
A wireless network capable of both VHF and HF band operation
All of the above.

G2E13 A Winlink Remote Message Server is a
Gateway.

G2E14 If you cannot decode an RTTY or other FSK signal even though it is apparently tuned in properly, the following could be wrong:

The mark and space frequencies may be reversed.
You may have selected the wrong baud rate.
You may be listening on the wrong sideband.
All these choices are correct.

G2E15 A common location for FT8 is
14.074MHz to 14.077 MHz.

SUBELEMENT G3 - RADIO WAVE PROPAGATION

[3 Exam Questions - 3 Groups]

G3A - Sunspots and solar radiation; geomagnetic field and stability indices

G3A01 The significance of the sunspot number with regard to HF propagation is that
higher sunspot numbers generally indicate a greater probability of good propagation at higher frequencies.

G3A02 The effect a Sudden Ionospheric Disturbance has on the daytime ionospheric propagation of HF radio waves is that **it disrupts signals on lower frequencies more than those on higher frequencies.**

G3A03 The increased ultraviolet and X-ray radiation from solar flares affects radio propagation on the Earth in about
8 minutes.

G3A04 The least reliable bands for long-distance communications during periods of low solar activity are
15 meters, 12 meters, and 10 meters.

G3A05 The solar flux index is
a measure of solar radiation.

G3A06 A geomagnetic storm is
a temporary disturbance in the Earth's magnetosphere.

G3A07 The 20-meter band usually supports worldwide propagation during daylight hours
at any point in the solar cycle.

G3A08 The effect a geomagnetic storm can have on radio propagation is
degraded high-latitude HF propagation.

G3A09 High geomagnetic activity can benefit radio communications because it creates
auroras that can reflect VHF signals.

G3A10 HF propagation varies periodically in a 28-day cycle because of
the Sun's rotation on its axis.

G3A11 A coronal mass ejection affects radio propagation in
15 hours to several days

G3A12 The K-index indicates
the short-term stability of the Earth's magnetic field

G3A13 The A-index indicates
the long-term stability of the Earth's geomagnetic field.

G3A14 The effect of charged particles that reach the Earth from solar coronal holes on radio communications is that
HF communication is disturbed.

G3B - Maximum Usable Frequency; Lowest Usable Frequency; short path and long path propagation; determining propagation conditions; ionospheric refraction

G3B01 If a sky-wave signal arrives at your receiver by both short path and long path propagation,
a slightly delayed echo might be heard.

G3B02 The factors affecting the MUF are:
Path distance and location
Time of day and season
Solar radiation and ionospheric disturbances
All these choices are correct.

G3B03 The frequency with least attenuation for long-distance skip propagation will be
just below the MUF. (Maximum useable frequency).

G3B04 A way to determine current propagation on a desired band from your station is
use a network of automated receiving stations to see where your transmissions are being received.

G3B05 When radio waves with frequencies below the MUF and above the LUF are sent into the ionosphere,
they are refracted back to the Earth.

REVIEW - PROPAGATION

G3B06 Radio waves with frequencies below the LUF
are completely attenuated before reaching the destination.

G3B07 LUF stands for
the Lowest Usable Frequency for communications.

G3B08 MUF stands for
the Maximum Usable Frequency for communications.

G3B09 The approximate maximum distance along the Earth's surface normally covered in one hop using the F2 region is
2,500 miles.

G3B10 The approximate maximum distance along the Earth's surface normally covered in one hop using the E region is
1,200 miles.

G3B11 When the LUF exceeds the MUF,
propagation via ordinary skywave communications is not possible over that path.

G3B12 During the summer, lower HF frequencies
typically have high levels of atmospheric noise or static.

G3C - Ionospheric regions; critical angle and frequency; HF scatter; near vertical incidence skywave (NVIS)

G3C01 The ionospheric region closest to the surface of the Earth is
the D region.

G3C02 The term "critical frequency" at a given incidence angle is
the highest frequency that is refracted back to Earth.

G3C03 The F2 region is mainly responsible for the longest distance radio wave propagation
because it is the highest ionospheric region.

G3C04 The term "critical angle" as used in radio wave propagation means
the highest takeoff angle that will return a radio wave to the Earth under specific ionospheric conditions.

G3C05 Long-distance communication on the 40-meter, 60-meter, 80-meter and 160-meter bands is more difficult during the day because
the D region absorbs signals at these frequencies during daylight hours.

G3C06 A characteristic of HF scatter signals is
they have a fluttering sound.

G3C07 HF scatter signals often sound distorted because
energy is scattered into the skip zone through several different radio wave paths.

G3C08 HF scatter signals in the skip zone are usually weak because
only a small part of the energy is scattered into the skip zone.

G3C09 The type of radio wave propagation that allows a signal to be heard in the transmitting station's skip zone is
scatter.

G3C10 Near Vertical Incidence Skywave (NVIS) propagation is
short distance propagation using high elevation levels.

G3C11 The ionospheric layer that is the most absorbent of long skip signals during daylight hours on frequencies below 10 MHz is
the D region.

SUBELEMENT G4 - AMATEUR RADIO PRACTICES

[5 Exam Questions - 5 groups]

G4A – Station configuration and operation

G4A01 The purpose of the "notch filter" found on many HF transceivers is
to reduce interference from carriers in the receiver passband.

G4A02 A benefit of using the opposite or "reverse" sideband when receiving CW is that
it may be possible to reduce or eliminate interference from other signals.

G4A03 A noise blanker works by
reducing receiver gain during a noise pulse.

G4A04 The plate current of a vacuum-tube RF power that indicates correct setting of amplifier's TUNE control is
a pronounced dip.

G4A05 The reason to use Automatic Level Control (ALC) with an RF power amplifier is
to prevent excessive drive.

G4A06 The purpose of an antenna tuner is to
increase power transfer from the transmitter to the feed line.

G4A07 When increasing receiver's noise reduction control,
received signals may become distorted.

G4A08 The correct adjustment for the LOAD or COUPLING control of a vacuum tube RF power amplifier is
desired power output without exceeding maximum allowable plate current.

G4A09 Delaying RF output after activating a transmitter's keying line to an external amplifier is to
allow time for the amplifier to switch to the antenna between the transceiver and the amplifier output.

G4A10 The function of an electronic keyer is the
automatic generation of dots and dashes for CW operation.

G4A11 An ALC system should be inactive when transmitting AFSK data signals
because the ALC action distorts the signal.

G4A12 A common use for the dual VFO feature on a transceiver is
to transmit on one frequency and listen on another.

G4A13 A reason to use the attenuator function that is present on many HF transceivers is
to prevent signal overload from strong incoming signals.

G4B - Tests and test equipment

G4B01 The item of test equipment that contains horizontal and vertical channel amplifiers is
an oscilloscope.

G4B02 An advantage of an oscilloscope versus a digital voltmeter is that
complex waveforms can be measured.

G4B03 The best instrument to use when checking the keying waveform of a CW transmitter is
an oscilloscope.

G4B04 The signal source connected to the vertical input of an oscilloscope when checking the RF envelope pattern of a transmitted signal is
the attenuated RF output of the transmitter.

G4B05 Volt meters have high input impedance because that
decreases the loading on circuits being measured.

G4B06 An advantage of a digital voltmeter as compared to an analog voltmeter is
higher precision.

G4B07 The signals used to conduct a two-tone test are **two non-harmonically related audio signals.**

G4B08 The transmitter performance parameter measured by a two-tone test is
linearity.

G4B09 An analog meter is preferred to a digital multimeter **when adjusting circuits for maximum or minimum values.**

G4B10 A directional wattmeter can determine
standing wave ratio.

G4B11 When an antenna analyzer is used for SWR measurements, connect it to the
antenna and feed line.

G4B12 Strong signals from nearby transmitters can affect an antenna analyzer because
received power interferes with SWR readings.

G4B13 An antenna analyzer can measure
the impedance of coaxial cable.

G4C - Interference to consumer electronics; grounding and bonding

G4C01 A **bypass capacitor** might be useful in reducing RF interference to audio frequency devices.

G4C02 A cause of interference covering a wide range of frequencies could be
arcing at a poor electrical connection.

G4C03 The sound heard from an audio device experiencing RF interference from a single-sideband phone transmitter is **distorted speech.**

G4C04 The effect on an audio device or telephone system if there is interference from a CW transmitter is
on-and-off humming or clicking.

G4C05 A cause of high voltages that produce RF burns is **the ground wire has a high impedance on that frequency.**

G4C06 The effect caused by a resonant ground connection is **high RF voltages on the enclosures of station equipment.**

G4C07 You should not use soldered joints in lightning protection ground connections because
a soldered joint will likely be destroyed by the heat of a lightning strike.

G4C08 To reduce RF interference caused by common-mode current on an audio cable,
Place a ferrite choke on the cable

G4C09 To avoid a ground loop,
bond equipment enclosures together.

G4C10 A symptom of a ground loop somewhere in your station could be
you receive reports of "hum" on your transmitted signal.

G4C11 To minimize RF "hot spots,"
bond all equipment enclosures together.

G4C12 Ground metal enclosures of station equipment
to ensure hazardous voltages cannot appear on the chassis.

G4D - Speech processors; S meters; sideband operation near band edges

G4D01 The purpose of a speech processor as used in a transceiver is to
increase the apparent loudness of transmitted voice signals.

G4D02 A speech processor affects a transmitted singlesideband phone signal because
it increases average power.

G4D03 An incorrectly adjusted speech processor can cause:
Distorted speech.
Excess intermodulation products.
Excessive background pickup.
All these choices are correct.

G4D04 An S meter measures
received signal strength.

G4D05 A signal that reads 20 dB over S9 compared to one that reads S9 on a receiver, means the signal is
100 times more powerful.

G4D06 The change in signal strength of one S unit is
6 dB.

G4D07 To change the S meter reading from S8 to S9, the power output of a transmitter must be increased
approximately 4 times.

G4D08 The frequency range occupied by a 3 kHz LSB signal when the displayed carrier frequency is set to 7.178 MHz is
7.175 to 7.178 MHz.

G4D09 The frequency range occupied by a 3 kHz USB signal with the displayed carrier frequency is 14.347 MHz is
14.347 to 14.350 MHz.

G4D10 When using 3 kHz wide LSB, your displayed carrier frequency should be
at least 3 kHz above the edge of the segment.

G4D11 When using 3 kHz wide USB, your displayed carrier frequency should be
at least 3 kHz below the edge of the band.

G4E - HF mobile and portable HF stations; alternate energy source operation

G4E01 A capacitance hat on a mobile antenna is
to electrically lengthen a physically short antenna.

G4E02 A corona ball on an HF mobile antenna is
to reduce high voltage discharge from the antenna tip.

G4E03 The fused power connections best for a 100 watt HF mobile installation would be
to the battery using heavy-gauge wire

G4E04 It is best NOT to draw the DC power for a 100 watt HF transceiver from a vehicle's auxiliary power socket because

the socket's wiring may be inadequate for the current drawn by the transceiver.

G4E05 The most limiting factor in HF mobile installation is **low efficiency of the electrically short antenna.**

G4E06 One disadvantage of using a shortened mobile antenna as opposed to a full-size antenna is the
operating bandwidth may be very limited.

G4E07 The following may cause interference to be heard in the receiver of an HF radio installed in a recent model vehicle:
The battery charging system.
The fuel delivery system.
The control computers.
All these choices are correct.

G4E08 Individual cells in a solar panel connect together in a **series-parallel configuration**.

G4E09 The approximate open-circuit voltage from a fully illuminated silicon photovoltaic cell is
0.5 VDC.

G4E10 The reason that a series diode is connected between a solar panel and a storage battery that is being charged by the panel is
the diode prevents self-discharge of the battery through the panel during times of low or no illumination

G4E11 With a lithium iron phosphate battery,
the solar panel must have a charge controller.

REVIEW – ELECTRICAL PRINCIPLES

SUBELEMENT G5 – ELECTRICAL PRINCIPLES

[3 Exam Questions – 3 Groups]

G5A - Reactance; inductance; capacitance; impedance; impedance transformation; resonance

G5A01 When inductive and capacitive reactance are equal in a series LC circuit,
resonance causes the impedance to be very low.

G5A02 Reactance is
opposition to the flow of alternating current caused by capacitance or inductance.

G5A03 Opposition to the flow of alternating current in an inductor is
Reactance

G5A04 Opposition to the flow of alternating current in a capacitor is
Reactance

G5A05 In an inductor,
as the frequency of the applied AC increases, the reactance increases.

G5A06 In a capacitor,
as the frequency of the applied AC increases, the reactance decreases.

G5A07 The inverse of impedance is called
admittance.

G5A08 Impedance is
the ratio of voltage to current.

G5A09 The unit used to measure reactance is the
Ohm.

G5A10 The following devices can be used for impedance matching at radio frequencies:
A transformer.
A Pi-network.
A length of transmission line.

All these choices are correct.

G5A11 The symbol to represent reactance is
X

G5A12 In an LC circuit at resonance,
the inductive reactance and capacitive reactance cancel.

G5B - The Decibel; current and voltage dividers; electrical power calculations; sine wave root-mean-square (RMS) values; PEP calculations

G5B01 A two-times increase or decrease in power is
approximately 3 dB.

G5B02 The way total current relates to the individual currents in a circuit of parallel resistors is that
it equals the sum of the currents through each branch.

G5B03 The electrical power, if 400 VDC is supplied to an 800-ohm load is
200 watts.

G5B04 The electrical power used by a 12 VDC light bulb that draws 0.2 amperes is
2.4 watts.

G5B05 The watts dissipated when a current of 7.0 milliamperes flows through a 1,250-ohm resistance are
approximately 61 milliwatts.

G5B06 The output PEP from a transmitter with 200 volts peak-to-peak across a 50-ohm dummy load connected to the transmitter output is
100 watts.

G5B07 The value of an AC signal producing the same power dissipation in a resistor as DC voltage of the same value is
the RMS value.

G5B08 The peak-to-peak voltage of a sine wave with an RMS voltage of 120.0 volts is
339.4 volts.

REVIEW - ELECTRICAL PRINCIPLES

G5B09 The RMS voltage of a sine wave with a value of 17 volts peak is
12 volts.

G5B10 The percentage of power loss that would result from a transmission line loss of 1 dB is
20.6 percent.

G5B11 The ratio of peak envelope power to average power for an unmodulated carrier is
1.00.

G5B12 The RMS voltage across a 50-ohm dummy load dissipating 1200 watts is
245 volts.

G5B13 The output PEP of an unmodulated carrier if an average reading wattmeter connected to the transmitter output indicates 1060 watts is
1060 watts.

G5B14 The output PEP of 500 volts peak-to-peak across a 50-ohm load is
625 watts.

G5C – Resistors, capacitors, and inductors in series and parallel; transformers

G5C01 A voltage appears across the secondary winding of a transformer when an AC voltage source is connected across its primary winding because of
mutual inductance.

G5C02 If you apply voltage to the secondary winding instead of the primary of a 4:1 voltage step-down transformer,
the input voltage is multiplied by 4.

G5C03 The resistance of a 10, 20 and 50-ohm resistor connected in parallel is
5.9 ohms.

G5C04 The resistance of a 100 and 200-ohm resistor in parallel is
67 ohms.

G5C05 The primary winding of a voltage step-up transformer is usually larger size than the secondary is to
accommodate the higher current in the primary.

G5C06 The voltage output of a transformer with a 500-turn primary and a 1500-turn secondary when 120 VAC is applied to the primary is
360 volts.

G5C07 The turns ratio of a transformer used to match an antenna's 600-ohm feed point impedance to 50-ohm cable is
3.5:1.

G5C08 The capacitance of two 5.0 nanofarad capacitors and one 750 picofarad capacitor connected in parallel is
10.750 nanofarads.

G5C09 The capacitance of three 100 microfarad capacitors connected in series is
33.3 microfarads.

G5C10 The inductance of three 10 millihenry inductors connected in parallel is
3.3 millihenrys.

G5C11 The inductance of a 20 millihenry inductor connected in series with a 50 millihenry inductor is
70 millihenrys.

G5C12 The capacitance of a 20 microfarad capacitor connected in series with a 50 microfarad capacitor is
14.3 microfarads.

G5C13 To increase capacitance,
add a capacitor in parallel.

G5C14 To increase inductance,
add an inductor in series.

SUBELEMENT G6 – CIRCUIT COMPONENTS

[2 Exam Questions – 2 Groups]

G6A – Resistors; capacitors; inductors; rectifiers; solid state diodes and transistors; vacuum tubes; batteries

G6A01 The minimum allowable discharge voltage for maximum life of a standard 12-volt lead-acid battery is
10.5 volts.

G6A02 The advantage of batteries with low internal resistance is
high discharge current.

G6A03 The approximate junction threshold voltage of a germanium diode is
0.3 volts.

G6A04 The advantage of an electrolytic capacitor is
high capacitance for a given volume.

G6A05 The approximate junction threshold voltage of a conventional silicon diode is
0.7 volts.

G6A06 Don't use wire-wound resistors in an RF circuit
the resistor's inductance could make circuit performance unpredictable.

G6A07 The operating points for a bipolar transistor used as a switch in a logic circuit are
saturation and cutoff.

G6A08 A characteristic of low voltage ceramic capacitors is
comparatively low cost.

G6A09 In MOSFET construction,
the gate is separated from the channel with a thin insulating layer.

G6A10 The element of a vacuum tube used to regulate the flow of electrons between cathode and plate is the
control grid.

G6A11 If an inductor is operated above its self-resonant frequency,
it becomes capacitive.

G6A12 The primary purpose of a screen grid in a vacuum tube is
to reduce grid-to-plate capacitance.

G6B - Analog and digital integrated circuits (ICs); microwave ICs (MMICs); display devices; RF connectors, ferrite cores

G6B01 The performance of a ferrite core at different frequencies is determined by
the composition, or "mix," of materials used.

G6B02 The term MMIC means
Monolithic Microwave Integrated Circuit.

G6B03 An advantage of CMOS integrated circuits compared to TTL integrated circuits is
low power consumption.

G6B04 The typical upper frequency limit for low SWR operation of 50-ohm BNC connectors is
4 GHz.

G6B05 The advantage of using a ferrite core toroidal inductor is:
Large values of inductance may be obtained.
The magnetic properties of the core can be optimized for a specific range of frequencies
Most of the magnetic field is contained in the core.
All of these choices are correct.

G6B06 An integrated circuit operational amplifier is an
analog device.

G6B07 An N connector is a
moisture-resistant RF connector useful to 10 GHz.

G6B08 When emitting light, an LED is
forward biased.

REVIEW – CIRCUIT COMPONENTS

G6B09 A liquid crystal display
has higher contrast in high ambient lighting than an LED.

G6B10 A ferrite bead reduces common-mode current on the shield of a coaxial cable by
creating an impedance in the current's path.

G6B11 An SMA connector is
a small threaded connector for signals up to several GHz.

G6B12 The connector commonly used for low-frequency of dc signal connections is
RCA phono.

SUBELEMENT G7 – PRACTICAL CIRCUITS

[3 Exam Questions – 3 Groups]

G7A Power supplies; schematic symbols

G7A01 The function of a power supply bleeder resistor is **it discharges the filter capacitors when power is removed.**

G7A02 The components used in a power supply filter network are
capacitors and inductors.

G7A03 The rectifier circuit that uses two diodes and a center-tapped transformer is a
full-wave.

G7A04 The advantage of a half-wave rectifier in a power supply is
only one diode is required.

G7A05 The portion of the AC cycle converted to DC by a half-wave rectifier is
180 degrees.

G7A06 The portion of the AC cycle converted to DC by a full-wave rectifier is
360 degrees.

G7A07 The output waveform of an unfiltered full-wave rectifier connected to a resistive load is
a series of DC pulses at twice the frequency of the AC input.

G7A08 An characteristic of a switchmode power supply as compared to a linear power supply is
high-frequency operation allows the use of smaller components.

7A09 Refer to figure G7-1 on the next page. The symbol in figure G7-1 that represents a field effect transistor is
Symbol 1.

G7A10 The symbol in figure G7-1 that represents a Zener diode is
Symbol 5.

G7A11 The symbol in figure G7-1 that represents an NPN junction transistor is
Symbol 2.

G7A12 The symbol in Figure G7-1 that represents a solid-core transformer is
Symbol 6.

G7A13 The symbol in Figure G7-1 that represents a tapped inductor is
Symbol 7.

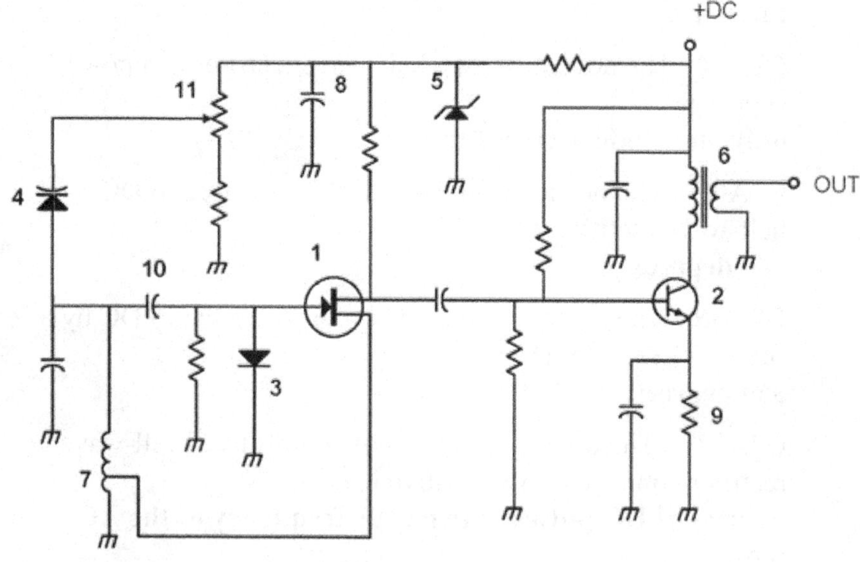

Figure G7-1

G7B - Digital circuits; amplifiers and oscillators

G7B01 The reason for neutralizing the final amplifier stage of a transmitter is
to eliminate self-oscillations.

G7B02 The listed class of amplifier with the highest efficiency is
Class C.

G7B03 The function of a two input AND gate is
output is high only when both inputs are high.

G7B04 In a Class A amplifier, the device conducts
100% of the time.

G7B05 A 3-bit binary counter has
8 states.

G7B06 A shift register is
a clocked array of circuits that passes data in steps along the array.

G7B07 The basic components of a sine wave oscillator are a
filter and an amplifier operating in a feedback loop.

G7B08 The efficiency of an RF power amplifier is determined by
dividing the RF output power by the DC input power.

G7B09 The frequency of an LC oscillator is determined by
the inductance and capacitance in the tank circuit.

G7B10 A linear amplifier is one in which
the output preserves the input waveform.

G7B11 A Class C power stage is appropriate for amplifying a modulated signal in
FM mode.

G7C - Receivers and transmitters; filters, oscillators

G7C01 To select one of the sidebands from the balanced modulator,
use a filter.

G7C02 The output of a balanced modulator is
double-sideband modulated RF.

G7C03 One reason to use an impedance matching transformer at a transmitter output is
to present the desired impedance to the transmitter and feed line.

G7C04 A product detector is used in a single sideband receiver

to extract the modulated signal.

G7C05 A direct digital synthesizer (DDS) characteristic is **variable output frequency with the stability of a crystal oscillator.**

G7C06 The advantage of a digital signal processing (DSP) filter compared to an analog filter is it
can create a wide range of filter bandwidths and shapes .

G7C07 A filter's attenuation inside its passband is
insertion loss.

G7C08 The parameter which affects receiver sensitivity is:
Input amplifier gain
Demodulator stage bandwidth
Input amplifier noise figure
All these choices are correct.

G7C09 The phase difference between the I and Q signals in a software-defined radio is
90 degrees.

G7C10 The advantage of using I-Q modulation with software-defined radios (SDRs) is it can
create all types of modulation with appropriate processing.

G7C11 Functions performed by software in a software defined radio (SDR) include:
Filtering
Detection
Modulation
All these choices are correct.

G7C12 The frequency above which a low-pass filter's output power is less than half the input power is the
cutoff frequency.

G7C13 The filter's maximum ability to reject signals outside its passband is called
ultimate rejection.

G7C14 The bandwidth of a band-pass filter is measured between the
upper and lower half-power.

SUBELEMENT G8 – SIGNALS AND EMISSIONS

[3 Exam Questions – 3 Groups]

G8A - Carriers and modulation: AM; FM, and single sideband; modulation envelope; digital modulation; overmodulation; link budgets and link margins

G8A01 Direct binary FSK modulation is generated
by changing an oscillator's frequency directly with a digital control signal.

G8A02 The process that changes the phase angle of an RF wave to convey information is
phase modulation.

G8A03 The process that changes the instantaneous frequency of an RF wave to convey information is
frequency modulation.

G8A04 The emission produced by a reactance modulator is
phase modulation.

G8A05 The type of modulation that varies the instantaneous power level of the RF signal is
amplitude modulation.

G8A06 A characteristic of QPSK31 is
It is sideband sensitive
Its encoding provides error correction
Its bandwidth is approximately the same as BPSK31.
All these choices are correct

G8A07 The phone emission that uses the narrowest bandwidth is
single sideband.

G8A08 An effect of overmodulation is
excessive bandwidth.

G8A09 The modulation used by the FT8 digital mode is
8-tone frequency shift keying.

G8A10 The term flat-topping when referring to a single sideband phone transmission means

signal distortion caused by excessive drive.

G8A11 The modulation envelope of an AM signal is
the waveform created by connecting the peak values of the modulated signal.

G8A12 QPSK modulation uses
digital data transmitted in 0, 90, 180 and 270-degrees phase shift to represent pairs of bits.

G8A13 A link budget is
the sum of transmit power and antenna gains minus losses as seen at the receiver.

68A14 Link margin is
the difference between received power level and minimum required signal level at the input to the receiver.

G8B - Frequency changing; bandwidths of various modes; deviation; intermodulation

G8B01 The mixer input varied to convert signals of different frequencies to an intermediate frequency is
a local oscillator.

G8B02 The term for interference from a signal at twice the IF frequency from the desired signal is
image response.

G8B03 Another term for the mixing of two RF signals is
heterodyning.

G8B04 The stage in a VHF FM transmitter that generates a harmonic of a lower frequency signal to reach the desired operating frequency is the
multiplier.

G8B05 The intermodulation products closest to the original signal frequencies are
odd-order.

G8B06 The total bandwidth of an FM phone transmission having 5 kHz deviation and 3 kHz modulating frequency is
16 kHz.

G8B07 The frequency deviation for a 12.21 MHz reactance modulated oscillator in a 5 kHz deviation, 146.52 MHz FM phone transmitter is
416.7 Hz.

G8B08 It is important to know the duty cycle of the mode you are using when transmitting because
some modes have high duty cycles which could exceed the transmitter's average power rating.

G8B09 It is good to match receiver bandwidth to the bandwidth of the operating mode because
it results in the best signal to noise ratio

G8B10 The relationship between transmitted symbol rate and bandwidth is
higher symbol rates require wider bandwidth.

G8B11 The combination of a mixer's input frequencies found in the output is the
sum and difference.

G8B12 The process that combines two signals in a non-linear circuit to produce unwanted spurious responses is
intermodulation.

G8B13 An odd-order intermodulation product of frequencies F1 and F2 would be
2F1-F2.

G8C – Digital emission modes

G8C01 The band amateurs share channels with unlicensed Wi-Fi service is
2.4 GHz.

G8C02 The digital mode used as a low-power beacon for assessing HF propagation is
WSPR.

G8C03 The part of a data packet containing the routing and handling information is the
header.

REVIEW - SIGNALS AND EMISSIONS

G8C04 Baudot code is
a 5-bit code with additional start and stop bits.

G8C05 In ARQ mode, a NAK response to a transmitted packet means
request retransmission of the packet.

G8C06 The result of a failure to exchange information due to excessive transmission attempts when using an ARQ mode is
the connection is dropped.

G8C07 The narrow-band digital mode that can receive signals with very low signal-to-noise ratios is
FT8.

G8C08 PSK31 **upper case letters use longer Varicode symbols and slow down transmission.**

G8C09 **If one mesh network microwave node fails, a packet may reach its target station via an alternate node.**

G8C10 Forward error correction (FEC) allows the receiver to correct errors
by transmitting redundant information with the data.

G8C11 The two separate frequencies of a Frequency Shift Keyed (FSK) signal are identified as
Mark and Space.

G8C12 The code used for sending PSK31 characters is
Varicode.

G8C13 A waterfall display with one or more vertical lines on either side of a digital signal indicates
overmodulation.

G8C14 On a waterfall display,
frequency is horizontal, signal strength is intensity, time is vertical.

G8C15 An FT8 signal report of +3 means
the signal-to-noise ratio is equivalent to +3dB.

G8C16 Digital voice modes are:
DMR, D-Star and SystemFusion.

SUBELEMENT G9 – ANTENNAS AND FEED LINES

[4 Exam Questions – 4 Groups]

G9A - Feed lines: characteristic impedance and attenuation; standing wave ratio SWR calculation, measurement and effects; antenna feed point matching

G9A01 The factors that determine the characteristic impedance of a parallel conductor antenna feed line are
the distance between the centers of the conductors and the radius of the conductors.

G9A02 High standing wave ratio
increases loss in a lossy transmission line.

G9A03 The characteristic impedance of "window line" parallel transmission line is
450 ohms.

G9A04 Reflected power at the point where a feed line connects to an antenna might be caused by
a difference between feed-line impedance and antenna feed-point impedance.

G9A05 In coaxial cable as the frequency of the signal it is carrying increases
attenuation increases

G9A06 RF feed line loss is usually expressed in
decibels per 100 feet.

G9A07 To prevent standing waves on an antenna feed line,
the antenna feed point impedance must be matched to the characteristic impedance of the feed line.

G9A08 If the SWR on an antenna feed line is 5 to 1, and a matching network at the transmitter end of the feed line is adjusted to 1 to 1 SWR, the resulting SWR on the feed line is
5 to 1.

G9A09 The standing wave ratio when connecting a 50-ohm feed line to a non-reactive load having a 200-ohm impedance would be

4:1.

G9A10 The standing wave ratio when connecting a 50-ohm feed line to a non-reactive load having a 10-ohm impedance would be
5:1.

G9A11 Transmission line loss affects SWR at the input to the line because
higher loss reduces SWR measured at the input to the line.

G9B - Basic dipole and monopole antennas

G9B01 With a random wire HF antenna connected directly to the transmitter,
station equipment may carry significant RF current.

G9B02 A common way to adjust the feed point impedance of a quarter-wave ground plane vertical antenna to be approximately 50 ohms is to
slope the radials downward.

G9B03 The radiation pattern of a quarter-wave ground-plane vertical antenna is
omnidirectional in azimuth.

G9B04 The radiation pattern of a dipole antenna in free space in the plane of the conductor is
a figure-eight at right angles to the antenna.

G9B05 The effect of antenna height on the horizontal (azimuthal) radiation pattern of a horizontal dipole HF antenna:
if the antenna is less than 1/2 wavelength high, the azimuthal pattern is almost omnidirectional.

G9B06 The radial wires of a ground-mounted vertical antenna system should be placed
on the surface of the Earth or buried a few inches below the ground.

G9B07 As a 1/2 wave dipole antenna is lowered below 1/4 wave above ground, the feed point impedance
steadily decreases.

G9B08 As the feed point impedance of a 1/2 wave dipole is moved from the center toward the ends,
the feed point impedance steadily rises.

G9B09 An advantage of a horizontally polarized as compared to a vertically polarized HF antenna is
lower ground reflection losses.

G9B10 The approximate length for a 1/2 wave dipole antenna cut for 14.250 MHz is
33 feet.

G9B11 The approximate length for a 1/2 wave dipole antenna cut for 3.550 MHz is
132 feet.

G9B12 The approximate length for a 1/4 wave vertical antenna cut for 28.5 MHz is
8 feet.

G9C - Directional antennas

G9C01 To increase the bandwidth of a Yagi antenna, use
larger diameter elements.

G9C02 The approximate length of the driven element of a Yagi antenna is
1/2 wavelength.

G9C03 On a three-element, single-band Yagi antenna, compared to the driven element,
the reflector is longer, and the director is shorter.

G9C04 Antenna gain in dBi is
2.15 dB higher than dBd figures.

G9C05 The effect of increasing boom length and adding directors to a Yagi antenna is
gain increases.

G9C06 This question was deleted from the pool.

G9C07 The "front-to-back ratio" in reference to a Yagi antenna means

the power radiated in the major lobe compared to the power radiated in the opposite direction.

G9C08 The "main lobe" of a directive antenna means **the direction of maximum radiated field strength from the antenna**

G9C09 The gain of two 3-element horizontally polarized Yagi antennas spaced vertically 1/2 wavelength apart typically compares to the gain of a single Yagi in that the gain is **approximately 3 dB higher.**

G9C10 The Yagi antenna design variables that could be adjusted to optimize forward gain, front-to-back ratio, or SWR bandwidth are:
The physical length of the boom.
The number of elements on the boom.
The spacing of each element along the boom.
All these choices are correct.

G9C11 A beta or hairpin match is **a shorted transmission line stub placed at the feed point of a Yagi antenna to provide impedance matching.**

G9C12 An characteristic of using a gamma match with a Yagi antenna is **it does not require that the driven element be insulated from the boom.**

G9D - Specialized antenna types and applications

G9D01 The type of antenna most effective as a Near Vertical Incidence Skywave (NVIS) antenna for short skip **is a horizontal dipole between 1/10 and 1/4 wavelengths above ground.**

G9D02 The feed point impedance of an end-fed half-wave antenna is **very high.**

G9D03 The direction of maximum radiation from a portable VHF/UHF "halo" antenna is **omnidirectional in the plane of the halo.**

G9D04 The primary purpose of antenna traps is
to enable multiband operation.

G9D05 An advantage of vertically stacking horizontally polarized Yagi antennas is
it narrows the main lobe in elevation.

G9D06 An advantage of a log periodic antenna is
wide bandwidth.

G9D07 On a log-periodic antenna,
length and spacing of the elements increase logarithmically along the boom.

G9D08 A "screwdriver" antenna adjusts its feed-point impedance
by varying the base loading inductance.

G9D09 The primary use of a Beverage antenna is
directional receiving for MF and low HF bands.

G9D10 An electrically small loop has nulls
broadside to the loop.

G9D11 A disadvantage of multiband antennas is
they have poor harmonic rejection.

G9D12 The common name of a dipole with a single central support is
inverted Vee.

G9D13 This question was deleted from the pool.

SUBELEMENT G0 – ELECTRICAL AND RF SAFETY

[2 Exam Questions – 2 Groups]

G0A - RF safety principles, rules and guidelines; routine station evaluation

G0A01 RF energy can affect human body tissue because
it heats body tissue.

G0A02 Properties important in estimating whether an RF signal exceeds the maximum permissible exposure (MPE) are:
Duty cycle.
Frequency.
Power density.
All these choices are correct.

G0A03 You can determine that your station complies with FCC RF exposure regulations:
By calculation based on FCC OET Bulletin 65.
By calculation based on computer modeling.
By measurement of field strength using calibrated equipment.
All these choices are correct.

G0A04 "Time averaging," in reference to RF radiation exposure, means
the total RF exposure averaged over a certain period.

G0A05 If an evaluation of your station shows RF energy radiated from your station exceeds permissible limits, you must
take action to prevent human exposure to the excessive RF fields.

G0A06 If your station fails to meet the FCC Rf exemption criteria,
you must perform an RF exposure evaluation.

G0A07 The effect of the modulation duty cycle when evaluating RF exposure is
a lower duty cycle permits greater power levels to be transmitted.

G0A08 The steps an amateur operator must take to ensure compliance with RF safety regulations when transmitter power exceeds levels specified in FCC Part 97.13 are to
perform a routine RF exposure evaluation and prevent access to any identified high exposure areas.

G0A09 The type of instrument that can be used to accurately measure an RF field is
a calibrated field strength meter with a calibrated antenna.

G0A10 If evaluation shows that a neighbor might receive more than the allowable limit of RF exposure from the main lobe of a directional antenna,
take precautions to ensure that the antenna cannot be pointed in their direction.

G0A11 If you install an indoor transmitting antenna,
make sure that MPE limits are not exceeded in occupied areas.

G0A12 Stations subject to the FCC rules on RF exposure are
all stations with a time-averaged transmission of more than one-milliwatt.

G0B – Station safety; electrical shock, grounding, fusing, interlocks, and wiring, antenna and tower safety

G0B01 The wire or wires in a four-conductor 240 VAC circuit that should be attached to fuses or circuit breakers are
only the hot wires.

G0B02 The minimum wire size that may be safely used for a circuit that draws up to 20 amperes of continuous current is
AWG 12.

G0B03 The size of fuse or circuit breaker appropriate to use with a circuit that uses AWG 14 wiring is
15 amperes.

G0B04 The station's lightning protection ground system should be located
outside the building.

REVIEW – SAFETY

G0B05 A Ground Fault Circuit Interrupter (GFCI) will disconnect AC power to a device if it senses **current flowing from one or more of the hot wires directly to ground.**

G0B06 The National Electrical Code covers **electrical safety of the station.**

G0B07 When climbing a tower using a safety belt or harness, **confirm that the belt is rated for the weight of the climber and that it is within its allowable service life.**

G0B08 Before climbing a tower that supports electrically powered devices,
make sure all circuits that supply power to the tower are locked out and tagged.

G0B09 Emergency generators should be located
in a well-ventilated area.

G0B10 A danger from lead-tin solder is
lead can contaminate food if hands are not washed carefully after handling the solder

G0B11 Lightning protection ground rods
must be bonded together with all other grounds.

G0B12 The purpose of a power supply interlock is
to ensure that dangerous voltages are removed if the cabinet is opened.

G0B13 Lightning arrestors should be located
where the feed lines enter the building.

~~~~~~

2023-2027 General Class FCC Element 3 Question Pool
Effective July 1, 2023
~~~~~~

BONUS MATERIAL LEARNING CW

Would you think it is impossible to learn a foreign language if it was only 26 words and count to 10? Probably not.

Boy Scouts was my first experience with CW. Unfortunately, I learned it all wrong and had to relearn it as a Ham. What went wrong?

In Boy Scouts, we memorized CW as dots and dashes. You had a chart and looked up every letter. The first exposure was visual, not audible. What's wrong with that? Your brain has to translate what it sees or hears into dots and dashes and then translate those into letters. It becomes a multi-step process. It is like learning to translate from English to Spanish to get to French.

I thought I understood it pretty well until someone sent Morse code by flashlight. It was blinking light to dots and dashes to letters. It was even worse when sent by waving a flag. I was lost.

Radio CW is audible. Learn to recognize the sound, not dots and dashes. "A" is not dot-dash. It is not even dit-dah. It is the sound of dit-dah. Learning the sound eliminates all the in-between translations.

For the same reason, do not learn that "A" sounds like "Ah-pull" or that the letter "A" has a short line and a long line. I've seen pictograms like children's alphabet blocks. These gimmicks introduce additional mental steps. Now you are going from English to Spanish to French to get to Russian.

Learn CW by hearing one or two letters at a time until you can immediately make the connection from the sound to the letter. Then go on to the next letters and build. This is called the Koch method.

LEARNING CW

Another impediment to my learning was the way we sent CW. At slow speeds "A" became the sound made by diiiiiiit-daaaaaaaaaah. Then, the next letter came immediately, with no time for the brain to work. The modern method is called Farnsworth timing.

Farnsworth timing sends the letters at least 20 words per minute[10], so each letter has one distinct sound. Dits and dahs may form a letter, but don't listen for the individual elements. The letter is one sound.

Farnsworth increases the space between letters and words to slow the pace. This does two things. Sending letters quickly reinforces a single sound as the letter. Spacing gives the brain extra time between letters and words to do the translation. Send using Farnsworth timing because that is how the other guy learned, as well. I send around 22-26 words per minute and slow down by increasing spaces.

Learning takes practice. In the beginning, listen to a code practice CD or audio file. K7QO offers a free course download on his website, K7QO.net. G4FON has a Koch trainer at G4FON.net. There are other sources, as well.

After learning the letters, recognizing words comes naturally. When reading, you do not see letters; your brain jumps to the word. "Word" is not "W-O-R-D." The same happens with Morse code. Learn to recognize your callsign, RST, 5NN, TU, 73 and other common "words" without thinking about the individual letters or the elements that make up the letters.

---

[10] Words per minute (WPM) is based on a 5 letter word. "Paris" is an often-used standard. Send "Paris" 20 times in a minute for 20 WPM.

Once you get the letters down (mostly), listen to learn the standard QSO pattern. Then, GET ON THE AIR! There is no better practice than making contacts. Real QSOs are exciting and won't seem like practice.

Getting on the air is the best way to practice.

FISTS CW Club and Straight Key Century Club (SKCC) promote CW, and you will find slow CW on the calling frequencies suggested on their web pages. Both FISTS CW Club and SKCC assign you a member number to exchange with other members and collect awards. It is a fun challenge.

Suggested frequencies to find slower CW include:
3.550 - 3.570 MHz
7.055 - 7.060 MHz
14.055 - 14.060 MHz
21.055 - 21.060 MHz
28.055 - 28.060 MHz

FISTS USA
FISTS Number 10,000

KNOWCW

USA Club Call of FISTS CW Club
Headquarters: PO BOX 47, Hadley MI 48440

Radio	Date	UTC	MHz	2-X	RST	Power	QSL
K4IA	5/13/06	1758	7 MHz	CW	599	100 W	Tnx / Pse

FIST members can get permission to use the FISTS CW Club callsign.

When starting out on CW, concentrate on the QSO Trinity first. The pattern is always the same, RST, QTH, name, so you know what to expect. With time, progress into more complex conversations. Try to match the speed of the other guy, but if you can't, "QRS" means "slow down" and "QRQ" means "speed up."

For more serious practice, tune to the W1AW Code Practice Sessions. These texts from *QST* magazine are harder to copy because the words are longer and not as predictable. ARRL offers code proficiency certificates that will look impressive on your wall. http://www.arrl.org/w1aw-operating-schedule

INDEX

INDEX

Made in the USA
Las Vegas, NV
13 October 2023

The easy way to pass the test is to focus on the correct answers and nothing else.

I call this "All Ham And No Spam."

Amateur radio license tests are multiple-choice with three wron answers and one right answer for each question. Traditional test-prep materials go through the questions and all of the possible answers. For the General test, you see 1,728 answers but 1,296 are wrong!

Why be confused and frustrated studying three wror answers for every one right answer?

Pass Your Amateur Radio General Class Test – The Easy Way is different. The focus is on the right answers and only the right answers. Since you never see the wrong answers, the right answers will pop out when you take the test.

It could

U.S. $21.9

ISBN 9798985673920

9 798985 673920

900